NEVADA BUREAU OF MIN
SPECIAL PUBLICATION 16

GEOLOGIC TOURS IN THE LAS VEGAS AREA

by

Becky Weimer Purkey
Ernest M. Duebendorfer
Eugene I. Smith
Jonathan G. Price
Stephen B. Castor

1994

Prepared jointly by
Nevada Bureau of Mines and Geology
and
Department of Geoscience, University of Nevada, Las Vegas

Mackay School of Mines

How to use the Trip Guides

Each of the trips is a loop beginning and ending in Las Vegas, North Las Vegas, or Henderson. A brief description of the highlights of each trip and total mileage is given at the beginning of each trip log.

Directions are given as "right" or "left" and as clock directions; for example, 12:00 is straight ahead and 9:00 is to the left.

Turnoffs to key roads, exhibits, etc. are noted at many mileage points. **Do not turn off unless instructed to do so**.

On the longer trips, you will be instructed to reset the odometer to 0.0 at some places along the route; this makes it easier for you to chose or omit portions of the trip and also reduces errors caused by variations in odometer calibration.

The text descriptions at the mileage points should be read by a passenger so that the driver can devote proper attention to driving.

Travel in the desert can be potentially dangerous for the unprepared traveler. Always carry extra water, maps, food, clothing, tools for emergency car repair, and signalling devices.

Please help protect the fragile environment of the desert and items related to its historical antiquity. Leave only footprints and, above all, enjoy this magnificent area!

For definitions of the terms used in the text please refer to the Glossary in the back of this book. The Bibliography, also located at the back of this book, provides a warehouse of additional sources of information on the topics covered in the trip guides.

PREFACE

Much of the research performed by the staff at the Nevada Bureau of Mines and Geology, the Department of Geoscience at the University of Nevada at Las Vegas, and the Bureau of Land Management is published in technical reports that are useful mainly to earth scientists; however, there are many people fascinated by the intriguing landscapes around Las Vegas who would not normally be aware of these reports, nor enjoy wading through the technical language in them. There are also plenty of photographic guides for this area already available on the racks of every bookstore in the Las Vegas area.

Geologic Tours in the Las Vegas Area is intended to fill a gap in the current collection of available publications on tourist attractions and the natural history of the Las Vegas area. Our goal was to provide a geologic guide for interested local citizens and tourists as they drive the main roads visiting the region's many sites of natural beauty and historical importance. The other half of that goal was to provide area schools with earth science information and ideas for field trips and field study areas. All that you really need to enjoy this publication is an interest in wanting to know more about the area's landscapes, geologic history, rock formations and mineral deposits you may live around or may just be vacationing in the midst of for a while.

The geology of the Las Vegas region is as varied and spectacular as you will find anywhere on Earth, but so is its rich cultural and natural history. This publication includes information on the area's cultural history dating back to prehistoric times. Conditions of climate (past and present) and the different plants and animals that thrive in the extremely varied geographic settings within this local area are also described.

Five trips are offered in this book. Total mileage and information on services along the routes are given in the introduction to each trip. Trip 1 highlights the spectacular Wilson Cliffs and Red Rock Valley area in the central Spring Mountains west of Las Vegas. Trip 2 takes the traveler to springs north of Las Vegas that were once the sites of vast glacial lakes, and then climbs through a series of life zones—desert through arctic alpine—in a drive through the northern Spring Mountains. Trip 3 heads east of Las Vegas past Frenchman Mountain and along Northshore Road in very distorted and brilliantly colored rocks to Overton and the Valley of Fire State Park. Trip 4 highlights the recent volcanic activity in the Hoover Dam and Boulder City area south of Las Vegas and includes a side trip further south to the historic mining district of Nelson and the site of the 1974 flash flood at Nelsons Landing on Lake Mohave. Along the way, classic features of the Basin and Range province can be observed. Finally, Trip 5 turns the traveler's focus to Las Vegas Valley and the recent geologic processes along with man's influence observable right in the city.

We hope that your questions about this area are answered in this publication. If you would like to read more on any of the subjects addressed herein—the geology, history, plants—please refer to the extensive list of references and additional sources of information at the end of the book. Technical geologic terms are explained in the glossary near the end of the book.

Acknowledgments—The authors are grateful to the individuals and organizations that contributed their varied talents and services to the preparation of this publication. Nevada Bureau of Mines and Geology staff include: Dick Meeuwig, who edited the manuscript; Kris Pizarro and Jan Walker, who produced the fine maps, geologic illustrations, and botanical drawings from the authors' sketchy rough drafts; Rayetta Buckley, who composed and typeset this publication; and John Bell and Don Helm, who provided information from their current research on the recent faulting and subsidence issues addressed in Trip 5.

Outside of the NBMG, Tom Purkey donated two weeks assisting in several field checks of every mileage point. Art Gallenson, pilot with Lake Mead Air in Boulder City, took one author on a smooth, but not uneventful, ride over the guidebook area to obtain aerial photographs. He graciously provided his camera when hers broke early in the flight. Stephen Rowland, Professor of Geology at the University of Nevada, Las Vegas kindly offered his support throughout the completion of this project and helped in providing slides and sketches for one of the trips.

Except as noted in the captions, all photographs were taken by the authors. Historic photographs were reproduced with permission from the Nevada Historical Society and the California Division of Mines and Geology.

We especially want to thank the knowledgeable individuals who took the time to read this document and make valuable suggestions that substantially improved the final product: Joseph V. Tingley, economic geologist with the Nevada Bureau of Mines and Geology; Leslie G. McMillion, consulting hydrologist in Las Vegas; and Maxine Shane, public affairs specialist with the Bureau of Land Management in Reno.

Without the generous financial support of the U.S. Department of the Interior, Bureau of Land Management, this guidebook would not have been published. We especially want to thank Larry Steward, Thomas Leshendok, and Neal Brecheisen of the Reno Office of the Bureau of Land Management for recommending this project for funding and helping expedite its completion.

Becky Weimer Purkey, Geologic Information Specialist
Nevada Bureau of Mines and Geology

Ernest M. Duebendorfer, Associate Professor of Geology
Northern Arizona University

Eugene I. Smith, Professor of Geology
University of Nevada, Las Vegas

Jonathan G. Price, Director/State Geologist
Nevada Bureau of Mines and Geology

Stephen B. Castor, Research Geologist
Nevada Bureau of Mines and Geology

January 1994

CONTENTS

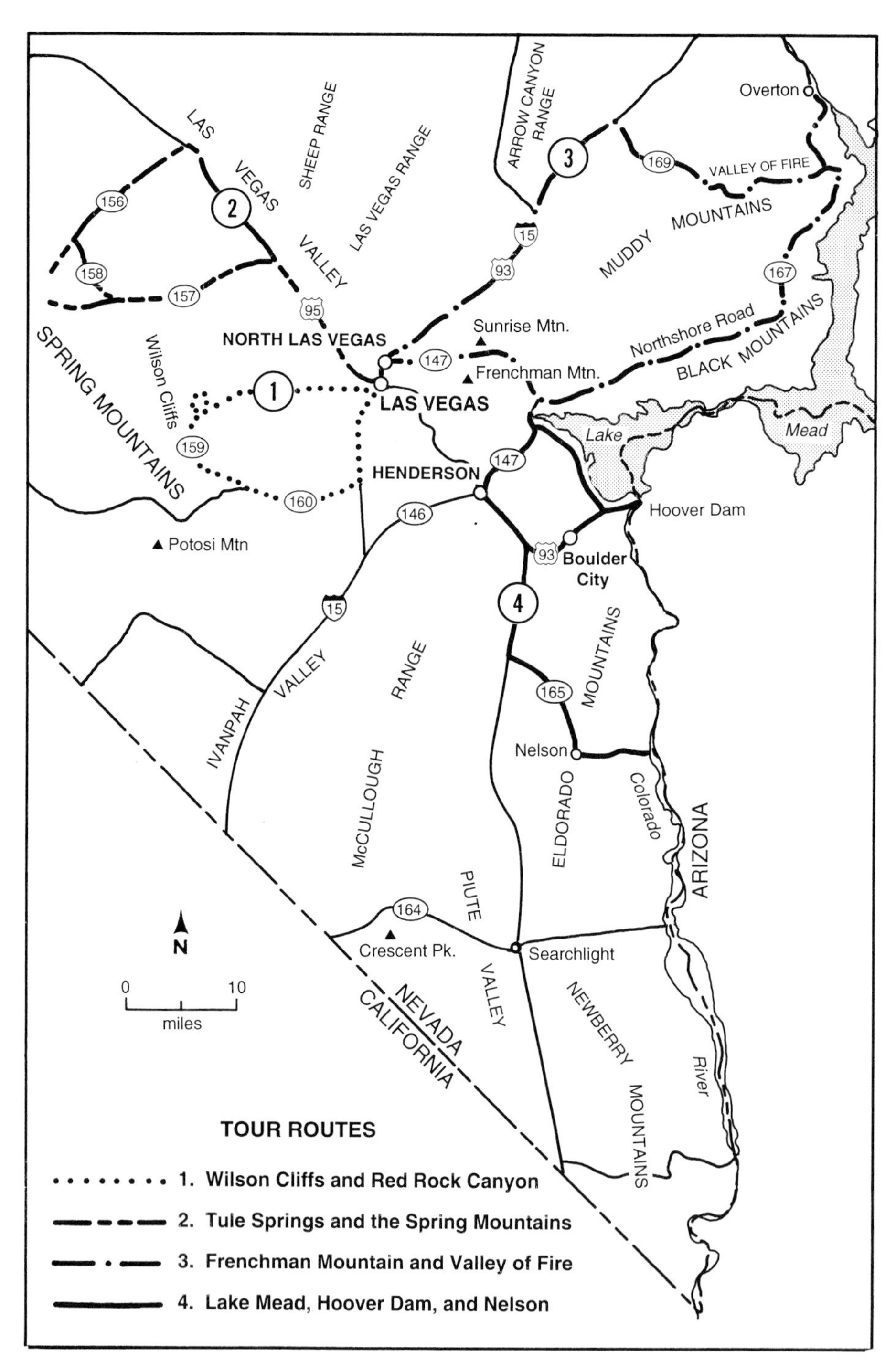

The route of Trip 5 is shown on page 133.

Introduction

The city of Las Vegas is located in Clark County in the southern tip of Nevada, a short distance from both California and Arizona. Geologic tours described in this road guide follow a network of paved roads that crisscross this part of Nevada. They cover an area extending from the nineteenth-century mining town of Nelson on the south to historic American Indian and Mormon settlements in the Virgin River Valley to the north. They also range between the Colorado River and Lake Mead on the east and the Spring Mountains on the west.

Setting

The Las Vegas area is in the Basin and Range physiographic province, a region characterized by a series of generally north-trending mountain ranges and intervening valleys filled with eroded sediments. The transition zone between the Basin and Range province on the west and the Colorado Plateau province on the east begins just east of Las Vegas. The Las Vegas area is a particularly good area to study geology. It contains many different types of rocks with ages that span nearly two billion years of geologic history. It also contains excellent examples of geologic structures and landforms. The rocks and structures are well exposed over large areas because of sparse vegetation and lack of soil cover in the desert environment.

One of the most delightful aspects of the Las Vegas area is the desert scenery, particularly in the evenings and early mornings, when shadows are long and the landscape acquires contrast and provides a sense of serenity that is well-known to long-time area inhabitants. This scenery—the mountains, canyons, valleys, alkali flats, and other features of the natural landscape—results directly from geologic processes of rock formation and erosion. In short, desert scenery is geology.

Geology is also the dominant influence on other characteristics of the land, including water and soil distribution, that ultimately determine where and how plants and animals live. In addition, geology is an important factor in the human environment. Early human inhabitants lived where they could find water, food, and natural shelter. Most of the later human settlements, including Las Vegas itself, were built adjacent to springs or other water sources, or sprang up near valuable mineral deposits. Although we are not as dependent on the natural environment as our ancestors, geology continues to influence our lives. Modern human shelters are generally built on the gently sloping floors of broad valleys; water courses with potential for episodic flooding are avoided or modified.

Most of the drainage in southern Nevada valleys is internal, that is, streams flow into valleys that have no external drainage. The Colorado River is an exception to this pattern. It drains an area along the southeastern margin of the state on its way to the sea. Elevations in the Las Vegas area range from a low of 450 feet along the valley of the Colorado River at the southernmost tip of the state to a high of 11,918 feet on Charleston Peak.

The climate ranges from hot and arid at the lowest elevations, to cooler, semiarid conditions in the higher basins, to more humid alpine climates in the high mountains. In most of the Las Vegas area, daytime summer temperatures can reach well over 100°F, but winter temperatures may plunge below freezing. Precipitation is less than 10 inches per year and occurs mainly from December to March in the form of storms generated by Pacific Ocean currents. Summer storms may also provide measurable precipitation, sometimes in violent downpours. Rain shadow effects are evident on the leeward side of the higher ranges where intermontane basins are arid to semiarid. Evidence for a much wetter and cooler climate just a few thousand years ago can be seen on several of the trips.

Las Vegas Valley and most of the other valleys in the Las Vegas area are in the Mojave Desert life zone, a transitional area between the Great Basin Desert to the north and the Sonoran Desert to the south. The Mojave Desert hosts a large variety of plants and animals that are well adapted to the hot, arid environment. Vegetation zones are mainly determined by elevation, but variations in slope, exposure, soil, temperature, precipitation, and drainage are also important. This can be observed especially well on Trip 2.

Plants along perennial streams and on playas located at or near the water table in the lowest parts of valleys are generally phreatophytes. They obtain water from near or below the water table, and include salt cedar, mesquite, salt grass, greasewood, rabbitbrush, pickleweed, and iodine bush. Phreatophytes discharge large amounts groundwater through transpiration. The alkaline flats are home to mixtures of phreatophytes and non-phreatophytes such as shadscale, bursage, desert holly, creosote bush, mesquite, Mormon tea, catclaw, alkali buckwheat, Mojave aster, and desert alyssum.

greasewood

shadscale

The lower slopes of alluvial fans that flank the mountain ranges, where the water table is considerably deeper, support communities of creosote bush, white bursage, catclaw, saltbush, little rabbitbrush, mallow, Mormon tea, sandpaper plant, brittlebush, littleleaf ratany, shadscale, fluff grass, and several species of cactus. Higher up on the alluvium and into the foothills, forests of Joshua trees and Spanish bayonet yucca are common, accompanied by blackbrush (the predominant small shrub) and various types of cactus and sagebrush. In riparian or marshy areas along streams at this elevation, reedbush, quailbush, mesquite, arrowweed, shadscale, wild grape, box thorn, Mormon tea, cattail, salt cedar, salt grass, bursage, indigo bush, desert willow, and various flowers are found.

Torrey saltbush

Above 4,500 feet, wooded areas of juniper and pinyon dominate. Above 7,000 feet, ponderosa pine, Douglas fir, white fir, and some bristlecone pine are found. Oak and aspen also make up this forest environment. High in the Spring Mountains are Englemann spruce, fir, small alpine shrubs, and grasses.

Douglas fir

White fir

Insects, spiders, reptiles, and the many mammals, from kangaroo rats to Bighorn sheep, are as varied as the plant life. While plants have adapted their leaves, needles, woody stems, germination cycles, and water-gathering root systems to the desert, the animals have adapted their diet, water sources, mating habits, and body morphology to thrive in this environment.

Cultural History

Archeologic discoveries at such places as Tule Springs north of Las Vegas, Gypsum Cave near Frenchman Mountain, and the Lost City near Overton give evidence of early habitation of this area from the Desert Culture of 10,000 years ago to the end of the Pueblo Culture in 1150 A.D. These areas are visited on Trips 3 and 5. The Paiute tribe entered the Las Vegas area around 1000 A.D.

Stewart Ranch in the 1880s (formerly Mormon Fort in 1855-57, and Las Vegas Ranch 1867-82). Photo courtesy of the Nevada Historical Society.

Fremont Street and railroad depot in Las Vegas in about 1910.
Photo courtesy of the Nevada Historical Society.

The Basic Magnesium complex in the 1940s.
Photo courtesy of the Nevada Historical Society.

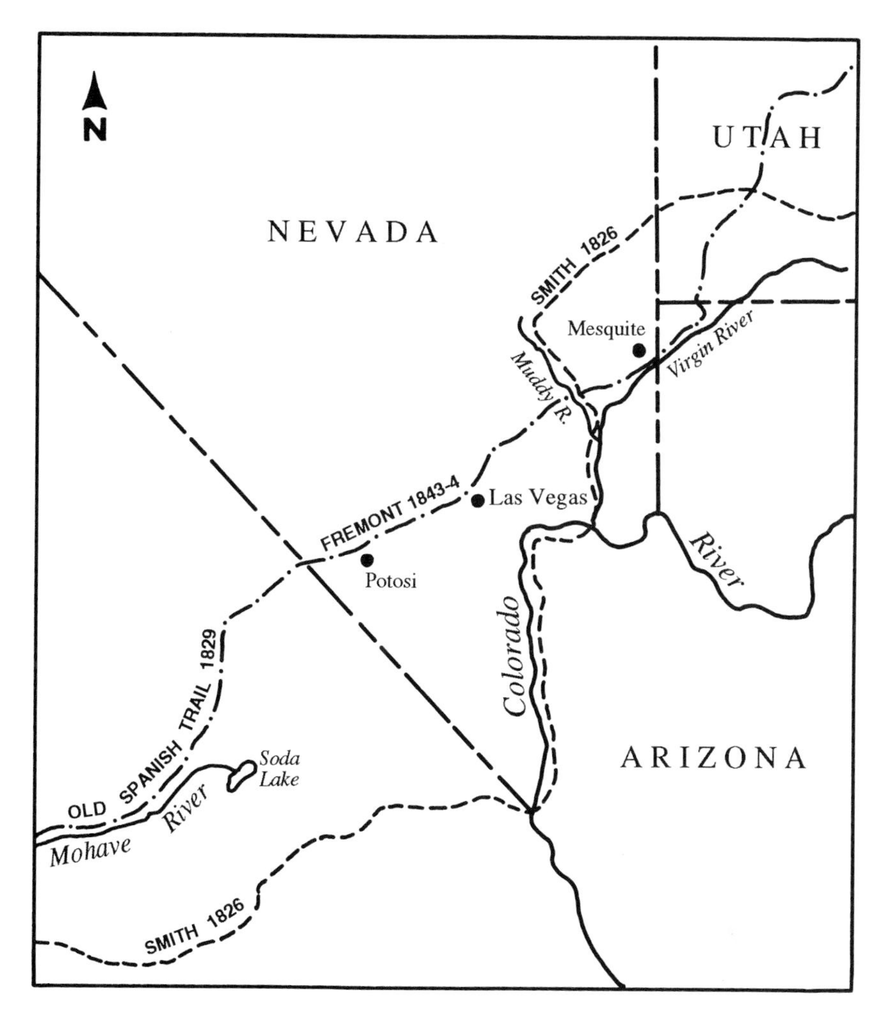

Trails of the early explorers and immigrants in southern Nevada.

The area became part of the Spanish Empire in the 1600s. The Spanish were navigating the Colorado River from the south as early as the 1700s and were the first white men to find gold in the Eldorado Canyon area. Francisco Garcés, a Spanish priest, is thought to have passed through Las Vegas Valley in 1776. After the Mexican Revolution in 1821, this territory became part of the Republic of Mexico.

By the 1830s early Mexican traders and immigrants on the Old Spanish Trail between Santa Fe and Los Angeles (which essentially follows the route of I-15 through this area) were regularly using the springs at Las Vegas and in Red Rock Valley. The Mexicans named the area Las Vegas, or *The Meadows*. Kit Carson and Jedediah Smith were also famous travelers through the area.

After the Mexican War in 1846-48, the Spanish Trail was abandoned by Mexican traders. With the signing of the Treaty of Guadalupe Hidalgo in 1848, title to this territory was transferred to the United States of America. Mormon missionaries began using a trail between Salt Lake City and California. The church established a settlement, Mormon Fort, at the springs in Las Vegas in 1855, but soon abandoned it. Afterward, ranches were established around the springs; of note were the Stewart and Kiel ranches.

With the establishment of the San Pedro, Los Angeles and Salt Lake Railroad through Las Vegas in 1903, the Las Vegas townsite was established with a population soon totaling about 2,000. The railroad also stimulated mining in the nearby districts of Nelson, Searchlight, and Goodsprings.

During World War II, when Basic Magnesium established an important industrial area in Henderson, the population of Las Vegas doubled to 17,000 people. Las Vegas Valley continues to grow, mainly as an entertainment mecca, and as of 1993 had a permanent population of about 855,000.

Geology

The Las Vegas area is unique in Nevada in that rocks representing parts of nearly 2 billion years of the Earth's history can be observed in a relatively small area. In the following trip logs, mention is made of some of the different rock types, how they were formed, and how old they are. However, brief overviews of some aspects of geology and of Las Vegas area geologic history are provided below.

The Three Rock Types

Rocks are made of minerals. A mineral is a naturally occurring, inorganic, solid element or combination of elements, with a definite chemical composition and a regular internal crystal structure. That is why minerals have certain definitive shapes and physical properties.

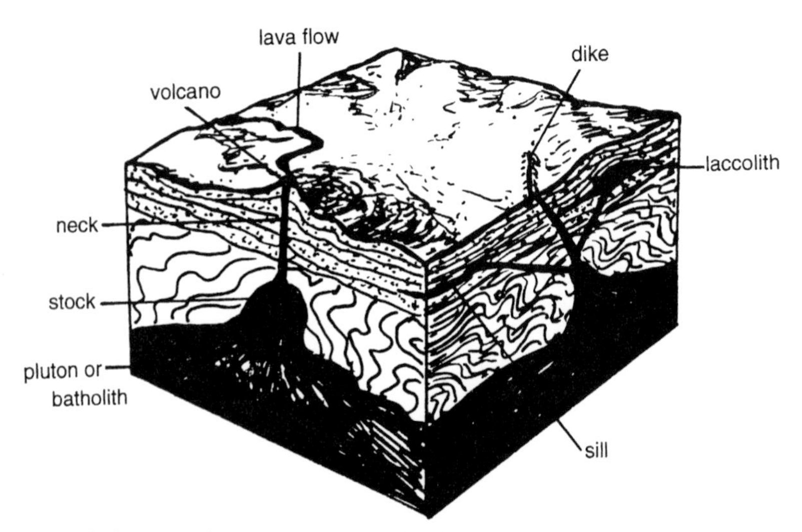

Block diagram showing the relationship between plutonic and volcanic rocks.

Rocks are classified into three major types depending on how they were formed. **Igneous rocks** are those that were previously molten, forming from magma (molten rock) from deep below the Earth's surface. Igneous rocks are given names on the basis of their composition and mode of formation. Most rising magma never reaches the surface, but cools slowly at depth forming masses of plutonic rock such as stocks, batholiths, and dikes. Granite is an example of plutonic rock that contains relatively large amounts of silica and alkali metal elements. Some magma does reach the surface of the Earth through openings in the crust, pouring out in calm flows or erupting violently and, in some cases, forming volcanoes. Magma that reaches the surface is called lava until it solidifies into volcanic rock. Basalt is a volcanic rock type that contains relatively little silica and large amounts of iron and magnesium.

Sedimentary rocks are formed in two ways. Clastic sedimentary rock, such as sandstone, forms from accumulations of particles or detritus of preexisting rocks that were been broken down and transported by the action of water, wind, or ice and deposited in a new location (in oceans, rivers, lakes, or desert basins). Nonclastic sedimentary rock is produced by chemically or biologically formed material precipitated out of certain bodies of water. Examples include limestone and evaporite rocks such as gypsum. In time, the deposited rock particles and precipitates harden to form solid rock.

Sedimentary rocks may contain fossilized remains of plants and animals, traces of their existence such as burrows or tracks, or preserved sedimentary structures such as crossbeds in sandstone or mudcracks in siltstone that tell us of the life and terrestrial environments that existed while that rock was being deposited. Fossils, particularly those types that existed for a geologically short time, are especially useful in correlating rocks of the same age around the world.

Finally, **metamorphic rocks** are preexisting rocks that have been changed by heat, pressure, and chemically active fluids, generally while in the solid state. Metamorphic rocks are physically different from the original rocks from which they were formed. They are commonly denser and tougher, and the original mineral grains have undergone changes in size or shape, or entirely new minerals have been formed. If high temperatures were involved, the former rocks may have been partially melted. Gneiss and schist are two common types of metamorphic rock.

All three rock types are abundant in the Las Vegas area. They record the processes that have shaped the desert landscape.

Geologic Structures

Many of the geologic structures that can be examined in the Las Vegas area are described in the road logs that follow. Faults, planar fractures in the Earth's crust that form during seismic activity (earthquakes), are common and well exposed in many places in southern Nevada. The Basin and Range province is one of the most seismically active parts of the world and during some parts of geologic history was probably even more active. Faults may be classified into several types on the basis of steepness and the motion along them. In the past, geologists recognized low-angle thrust faults and high-angle normal and strike-slip faults as important structural features in the Las Vegas area. Recently, low-angle normal or detachment

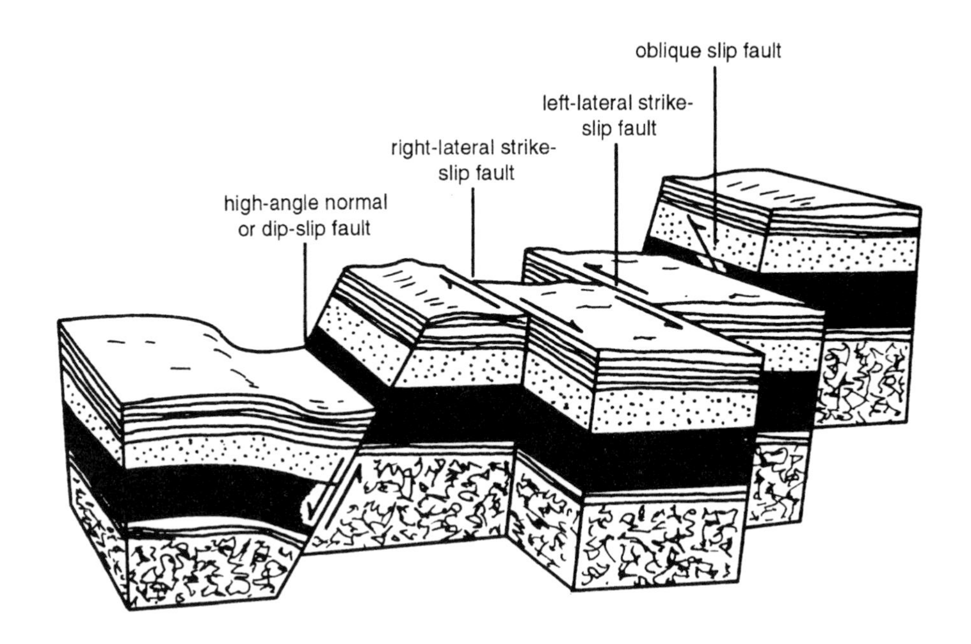

faults, which commonly have planar or curved normal faults in their upper plates, have been found to be highly significant structural features in the area.

Folds result from the flexing or wrinkling of sedimentary strata, and examples of different types of folds are present in southern Nevada. Upwardly convex folds are called anticlines, and upwardly concave folds are synclines. Folds that are tilted on their sides so that some of the strata are upside down (older rocks overlying younger rocks) are called overturned folds, and are often associated with thrust faults.

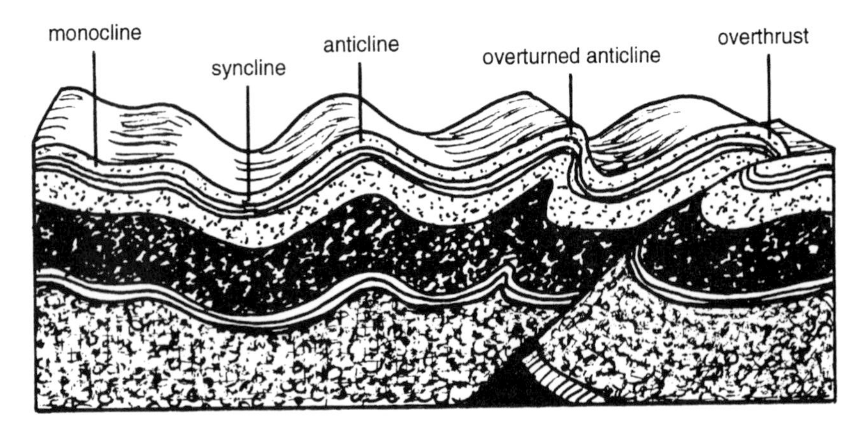

Types of folds and an overthrust fault (the result of rupture of an overturned anticline).

Plate Tectonics

Early in the twentieth century, on the basis of physical and geologic correlations between continents, some scientists proposed that the Earth's landmasses were mobile, sliding slowly about on the Earth's surface. This theory, called continental drift, was largely ignored in the United States until the 1960s, when new data were collected that convinced most scientists that the continents and the rocks of the ocean floor were indeed moving at rates of a few centimeters per year. Since that time many new concepts have

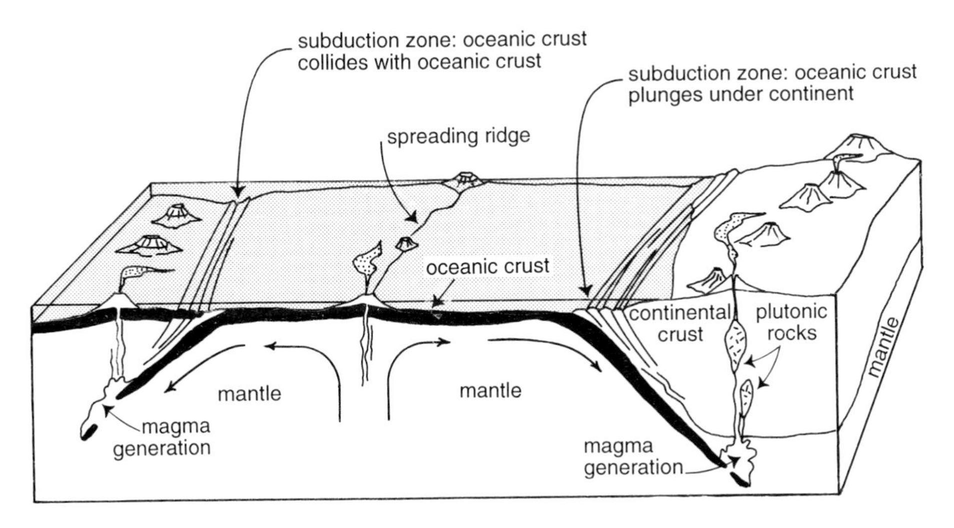

Simplified crustal block diagram showing plate tectonic processes at spreading ridges and subduction zones.

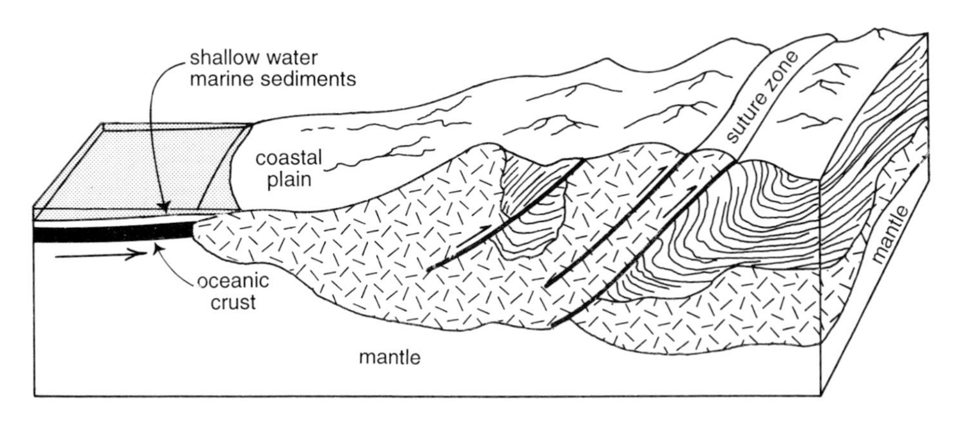

Simplified crustal block diagram showing a stable continental margin on the left and continental-continental collision on the right.

Major Divisions of Geologic Time

Era	Period	Subperiod	Epoch / Period	Base (age)	Origin of name
CENOZOIC	Quarternary	Neogene	Holocene	0.01 Ma	The several geologic eras were originally named Primary, Secondary, Tertiary, and Quaternary. The first two names are no longer used; Tertiary and Quaternary have been retained and used as period designations.
			Pleistocene	1.6 Ma	
	Tertiary (T)		Pliocene	5.3 Ma	
			Miocene	23.7 Ma	
		Paleogene	Oligocene	36.6 Ma	
			Eocene	57.8 Ma	
			Paleocene	66 Ma	
MESOZOIC			Cretaceous (K)	138 Ma	Derived from Latin word for chalk (creta) and first applied to extensive deposits that form white cliffs along the English Channel.
			Jurassic (J)	205 Ma	Named for the Jura Mountains, located between France and Switzerland, where rocks of this age were first studied.
			Triassic (Ŧ)	250 Ma	Taken from word "trias" in recognition of the threefold character of these rocks in Europe.
PALEOZOIC			Permian (P)	290 Ma	Named after the ancient Kingdom of Permia in Russia, where these rocks were first studied.
			Pennsylvanian (ℙ)	330 Ma	Named after the State of Pennsylvania where these rocks have produced much coal.
			Mississippian (M)	355 Ma	Named for the Mississippi River valley where these rocks are well exposed.
			Devonian (D)	405Ma	Named after Devonshire, England, where these rocks were first studied.
			Silurian (S)	435 Ma	Named after Celtic tribes, the Silures and Ordovices, that lived in Wales during the Roman Conquest.
			Ordovician (O)	510 Ma	
			Cambrian (Є)	570 Ma	Taken from Roman name for Wales (Cambria) where rocks containing the earliest evidence of complex forms of life were first studied.
PRECAMBRIAN (pЄ)			Proterozoic (Ᵽ)	2,500 Ma	The time between the birth of the planet and the appearance of complex forms of life. More than 80 percent of the Earth's estimated $4^1/2$ billion years is Precambrian.
			Archean (A)	4,550 Ma	

DOMINANT LIFE

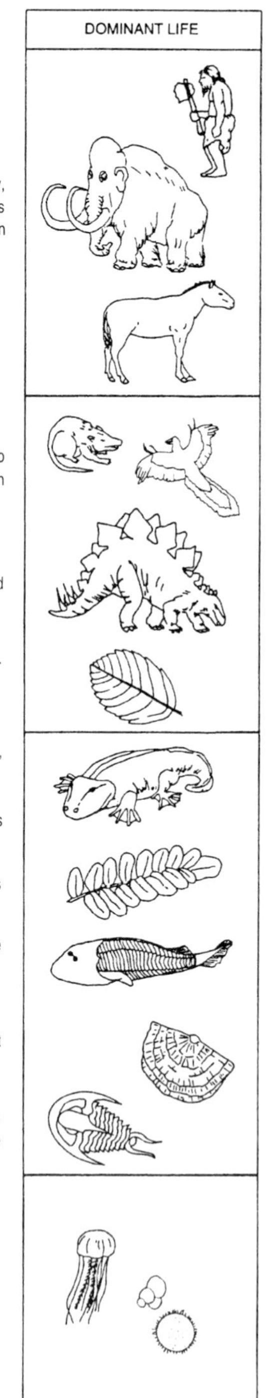

Ma = Mega-annum = million years

evolved that include continental drift in an overall theory of crustal movement called plate tectonics.

In plate tectonics theory, new oceanic crust is generated by magma emplaced into the sea floor at spreading ridges. Carpets of this oceanic crust move slowly away from the spreading ridges, possibly impelled by convection cells in the mantle, plastic rock beneath the crust, in a configuration much like conveyor belts. As new crust forms at spreading ridges, it is consumed in areas called subduction zones, some of which are at continental margins. Downward moving (subducted) oceanic crust is pushed into the mantle at continental margins, producing magma that rises through the continental crust to become plutonic or volcanic rocks.

Margins between oceanic and continental crust are not always subduction zones, and there are stable plate margins where movement of the oceanic plate may be pushing the adjacent continent. In some areas, continental masses have been pushed together by such movement, a process called continental collision. During recent geologic time, for example, India has been in collision with Asia, producing the massive Himalaya Mountains as a result of crustal buckling. Geologists think that continental masses have collided many times throughout the Earth's history, and that this is one of the principal ways that large continents are produced.

Plate tectonic movements are also responsible for the separation of continents along intercontinental rifts, where the land is pulled apart because of the development of a new spreading zone. The East African rift system is a modern example.

Geologic History

Some geologic history of this area is essential to understanding the rock formations and relationships seen on the trips. The geologic history of the Las Vegas area can be divided into four major divisions of geologic time: the Proterozoic, the Paleozoic, the Mesozoic, and the Cenozoic.

Proterozoic Rocks—The Basement

Geologists generally apply the term *basement* to old metamorphic and igneous rocks that make up a complexly deformed footing upon which more ordered sedimentary strata are deposited. The oldest rocks in the Las Vegas area are gneiss and schist that geologists believe were originally deposited as sediments and volcanic rocks 1.7 to 1.8 billion years ago during Proterozoic time. These rocks contain minerals that show that they were metamorphosed by intense heat and pressure. Various theories have been advanced to show how these rocks were combined, some say by repeated episodes of continental collision to form a huge land mass, or megacontinent, in Proterozoic time. About 1.4 billion years ago, large amounts of granitic magma were emplaced in these metamorphic rocks during a period of possible continental rifting and widespread igneous activity in the ancestral North American continent.

Extensive exposures of Proterozoic metamorphic and igneous rocks occur to the south and east of Las Vegas. Outcrops of these rocks can be observed on Trips 3 and 4.

The Paleozoic—Tropical Seas

During the Paleozoic Era, southern Nevada and much of the eastern Great Basin region was at the edge of the North American continent. The earliest Paleozoic rocks are clastic sedimentary rocks. In the Las Vegas area, Paleozoic seas lapping on the Proterozoic bedrock of the continent deposited beach deposits of the 600 million-year-old Tapeats Sandstone. This was followed by the deposition of the Pioche Shale, which locally contains abundant early Cambrian trilobite fossils. However, the Paleozoic in southern Nevada was mainly an era of geologic quiescence and nonclastic sedimentary deposition, marked by slow accumulation of limestone and dolomite in ancient shallow tropical seas that were similar to shallow parts of the present-day Caribbean. Beds of particularly pure Paleozoic limestone and dolomite are mined and processed into lime near Las Vegas.

Late in the Paleozoic, during the Permian Period, limestone deposition gave way to deposition of sandstone and gypsum. The Toroweap and Kaibab Formations, which mainly consist of limestone with abundant brachiopod and crinoid fossils, also contain sandstone and shale with associated gypsum beds. Gypsum in the Kaibab Formation is mined at two places near Las Vegas.

Sections of Paleozoic rock can be observed on Trips 1, 2, and 3.

The Mesozoic—Forests and Deserts

The Mesozoic Era, the age of the dinosaurs, was marked in southern Nevada by a change from marine to continental sedimentary deposition. Rocks in the lower part of the Triassic Moenkopi Formation contain fossils that indicate marine deposition, and these mark the last time that southern Nevada lay under the ocean. The Moenkopi was succeeded by the Chinle Formation, mainly clastic continental rocks that contain remains of ancient forests. Chinle deposition was followed by deposition of the Aztec Sandstone, a thick accumulation of wind-blown desert sand, whose fiery red outcrops occur to the west and east of Las Vegas and can be seen on Trips 1 and 3. The youngest Mesozoic formation, the Cretaceous Baseline Sandstone, is mined to produce silica sand near Overton.

The Mesozoic was also a time of significant regional change in the configuration of the earth s crust. Beginning in the early Mesozoic, easterly moving rocks of the Pacific oceanic crust began to descend beneath the westerly moving North American continent along a subduction zone. This resulted in intense magmatic activity that produced the granitic rocks of the Sierra Nevada and also caused compression, or horizontal squeezing, of rocks to the east that were previously laid down in the Paleozoic sea. The Mesozoic in southern Nevada was an era of uplift, large-scale folding of sedimentary rock strata, and thrust faulting caused by this compression. Some of the thrust faults can be seen on Trips 1, 2, and 3.

The Cenozoic—A Tug-of-War

During the Cenozoic Era, the Las Vegas area underwent a second major change in the style of geologic movement. During the early part of this era, much of the western United States was probably a high plateau,

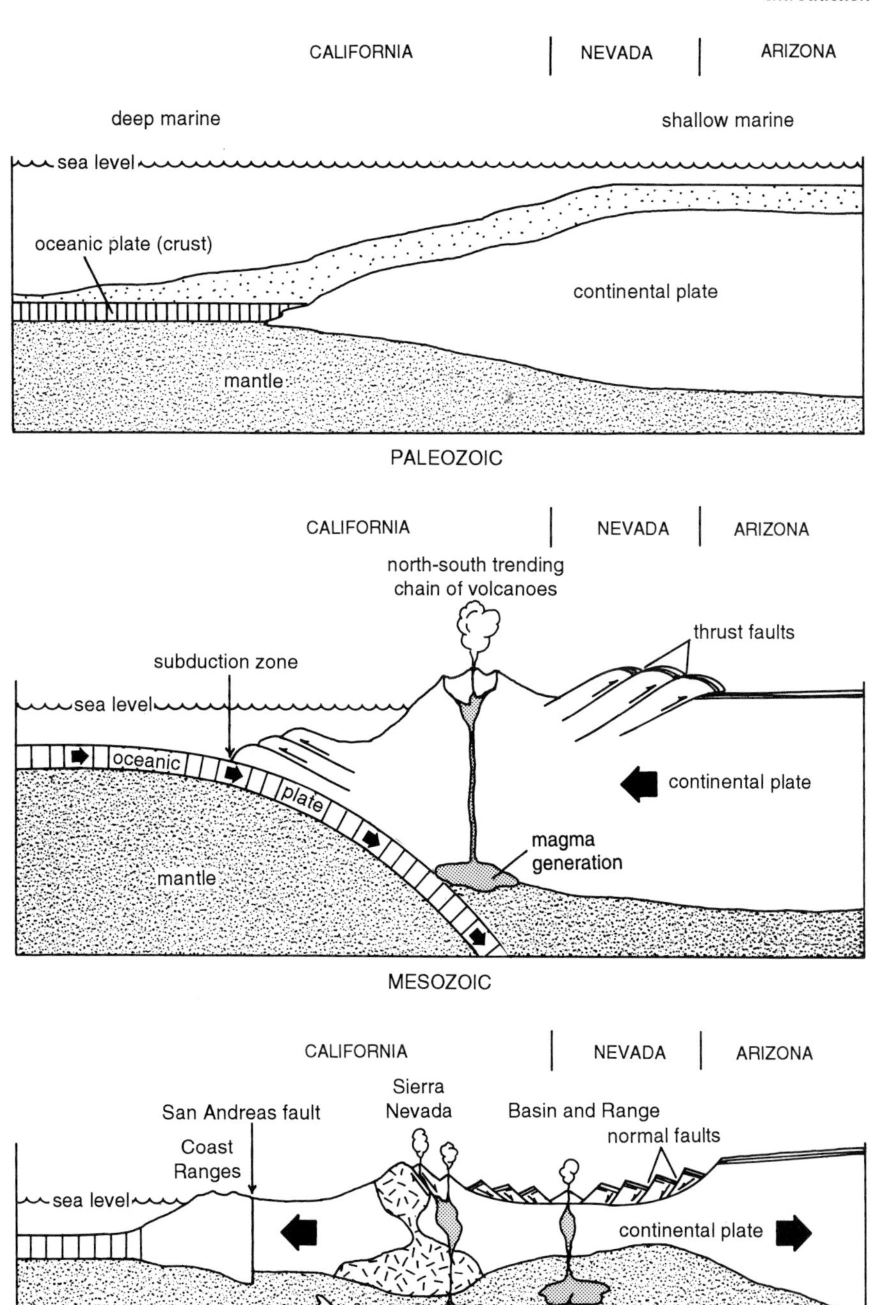

Cross sections from the Pacific Ocean through the present-day site of Las Vegas showing geologic processes at work about 500 million years ago (Paleozoic Era), about 100 million years ago (Mesozoic Era), and about 5 million years ago (Cenozoic Era) .

with erosion outstripping deposition. However, as the Pacific oceanic crust continued to push under the west coast of North America, the region underwent extensional deformation—meaning that it began to be literally pulled apart. The rocks were tilted, folded, and broken by faults during this deformation. Geologists believe that rocks that make up the Sierra Nevada were much closer to those of the Colorado Plateau in the early part of Cenozoic time than they are today. In southern Nevada, total east-west extensional movement is estimated at about 150 miles. During the latter part of the Cenozoic (about the last 20 million years), extensional forces produced the mountain ranges and intervening valleys that are characteristic of the Basin and Range province. Nearly all mountain ranges in Nevada are bounded by at least one fault, and these faults are considered to be active, moving during major earthquakes every few thousand years.

Crustal extension in southern Nevada resulted in the deposition of clastic and nonclastic sedimentary rocks of the Horse Spring Formation in fault-bounded basins in the Lake Mead area between about 17 and 12 million years ago. Horse Spring Formation strata were later tilted by extensional faulting, but clastic sedimentary rocks of the 10- to 5-million-year-old Muddy Creek Formation are largely undeformed. Volcanic activity also occurred between about 17 and 5 million years ago in southern Nevada as magma rose from depth along vents and fissures in the extensionally thinned crust. Volcanic rocks and landforms can be seen on Trips 3 and 4.

Willow Springs picnic area.

A pond at Tule Springs, with the Las Vegas Range in the background.

View of the extensive Desert National Wildlife Range looking northeast from the Desert Viewpoint.

Aerial view looking northeast. Gray Paleozoic limestone in foreground is separated from the red Aztec Sandstone by the east-trending Arrowhead fault in the middle of the flat valley in the middle of the photo.

Unconformity between red Miocene-age Muddy Creek Formation (bottom) and tan Quaternary sediments (top).

Black basalt boulders littering outcrops of red Aztec Sandsone.

Rogers Spring.

Creosote bush.

Rock varnish and petroglyphs at Mouse's Tank.

Petroglyphs at Mouse's Tank.

Lake Las Vegas and Lava Butte.

Looking northeast at Las Vegas Wash Marina and Muddy Mountains in the distance.

Looking east from the west side of Saddle Island, the detachment fault is revealed by changes in the color of the rocks. The red-brown rocks on the left (north) form the upper plate; green rocks on the right (south) are in the lower plate.

Looking west at the flanks of the River Mountains stratovolcano north of Boulder City.

Teddy Bear cholla at Nelson.

Erosional spires developed in Pleistocene gravels in Techatticup Wash.

TRIP 1—WILSON CLIFFS AND RED ROCK CANYON

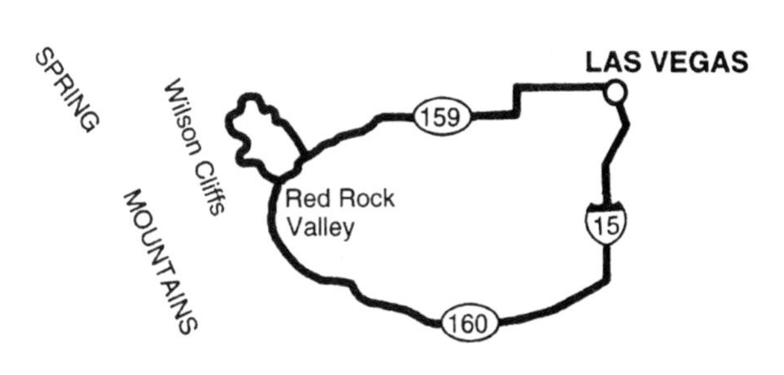

This trip takes you past the spectacular Wilson Cliffs on the west side of Las Vegas in the southern Spring Mountains. The colorful red and white rocks are host to beautiful springs that issue from hidden canyons, hiking trails, rich archaeological history, wild burros, and Joshua tree forests. Geologic highlights include close-up observations of the Aztec Sandstone and the thrust faults that occurred in this area on a gigantic scale from Mesozoic to early Cenozoic time, an operating gypsum mine, and locations where companies drilled for oil. The trip is about 50 miles in length. Gasoline is available at several locations near the start of the route. Water is available at the state parks and small towns along the way and at the Bureau of Land Management Visitor Center at Red Rock Canyon National Conservation Area.

0.0 From downtown Las Vegas, drive south on Interstate 15, turn right onto State Route 160, and **set odometer to 0.0 at the truck stop at the intersection of Industrial Road and Nevada State Route 160.**

2.5 Railroad crossing. In 1929, the first known petroleum exploration well in Clark County was drilled a few miles north of here in a geologic structure called the Arden dome. Exploration geologists have been drilling sporadically in this southern Nevada region hoping to find petroleum in a zone of thrust-faulted rocks. Known as the Overthrust Belt, this zone may extend from Alaska to Central America. Oil has been found in this belt in Wyoming, but so far there have been no significant shows found in this geologic terrain in Nevada. More sites of drilling are passed on Trip 3.

4.6 The impressive Wilson Cliffs, which form the southern end of the Spring Mountains, are straight ahead. The 2,000-foot high cliffs are composed dominantly of red and white Aztec Sandstone of Jurassic age (upper photo on the front cover). The Aztec Sandstone was probably deposited about 180 million years ago.

On the skyline is a series of dark gray rock layers above the Aztec Sandstone. These strata are limestone and dolostone of the Cambrian Bonanza King Formation. The sequence of rocks exposed in the Wilson Cliffs is out of normal stratigraphic order; that is, older rocks are resting upon younger rocks. This unusual arrangement cannot result from normal depositional processes; it indicates the presence of a major fault between the two layers. The fault surface is inclined gently downward to the west and places the older Cambrian rocks on top of younger Jurassic rocks.

Wilson Cliffs looking west from State Route 160.

Faults that place older rocks on top of younger rocks are known as reverse faults, or thrust faults if they are inclined at low angles. Thrust faults result from compressional forces within the Earth's crust.

This particular thrust fault is known as the Wilson Cliffs thrust which is part of the well-known Keystone thrust system. Because of its geological importance and spectacular exposure—it appears as a knife-sharp contact from the air— it is one of the most widely photographed thrust faults in the world.

The Keystone thrust system is one of a series of thrust faults in southern Nevada that collectively transported strata—originally 3 to 4 miles thick—tens of miles eastward. Movement along these great thrust faults probably occurred during the middle of the Cretaceous Period, although the exact age of activity on these faults remains a point of controversy among geologists.

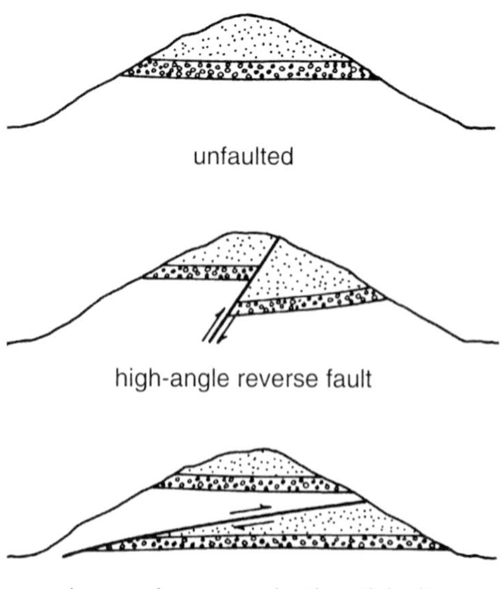

Oblique aerial photograph looking north over the Wilson Cliffs thrust. Charleston Peak in the northern Spring Mountains can be seen on the horizon in the center of the photo.

Charleston Peak (11,918 feet) at 2:30 is the highest peak in the Spring Mountains. It is usually snow covered from November through April. The prominent ridge at 11:00 is Potosi Mountain (8,512 feet).

10.1 **Intersection with State Route 159. Turn right (north) toward Blue Diamond and Red Rock Canyon.**

10.8 James Hardie Blue Diamond gypsum mine ahead on the right. Gypsum is extracted from a layer in the upper part of the Permian Kaibab Limestone. Gypsum, which is hydrated calcium sulfate ($CaSO_4.2H_20$), is formed in arid environments, in this

James Hardie Blue Diamond gypsum mine.

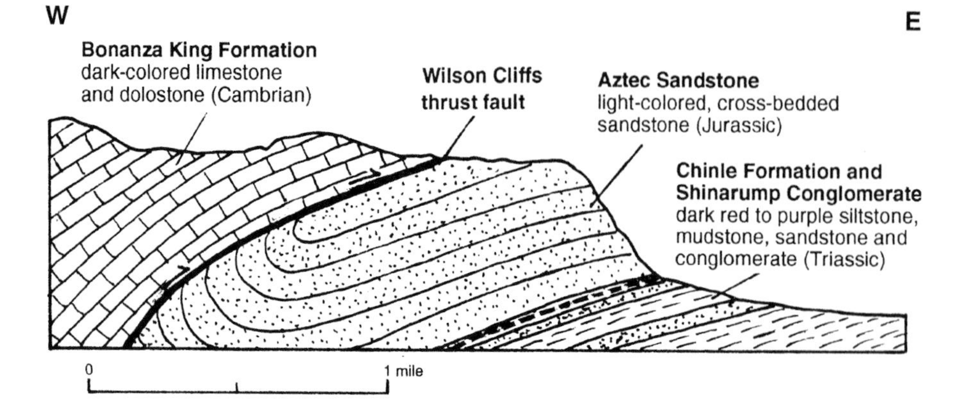

Cross section of the Wilson Cliffs thrust.

case most likely along the shores of the Permian ocean. Gypsum is used in the construction industry in wallboard, stucco, caulking, plaster of paris, and paint. Gypsum has been mined in this area since 1925.

The route continues west through strata that are dipping gently (10°) to the west. Because of the westward tilt of these strata, one encounters successively younger rocks to the west. For example, the rocks in the vicinity of the gypsum mine are Pennsylvanian and Permian in age (280 to 245 million years); the rocks of the Wilson Cliffs are Jurassic Aztec Sandstone.

At the narrows in the road, the ridge forming unit is the Permian Kaibab Limestone which is easily recognized by conspicuous brown concretions of chert. Concretions may form within the environment in which sediments accumulate by precipitation of mineral material around a nucleus, perhaps a plant or shell fragment, prior to consolidation of the rock. They may also form by replacement of part of the rock after consolidation. The Kaibab Limestone is the layer that forms the rim of the Grand Canyon. Fossil evidence indicates that it was deposited about 250 million years ago in a warm shallow sea similar to the environment that exists today near the Bahamas. The widespread distribution of the Kaibab Limestone indicates the great extent of this former shallow sea.

12.8 Entering Red Rock Canyon National Conservation Area administered by the U.S. Department of the Interior's Bureau of Land Management (BLM). All items within the area are protected. Please enjoy the area but do not remove any natural items.

12.9 Town of Blue Diamond on the left.

13.7 Good view of the Wilson Cliffs thrust.

14.0 The valley ahead is formed in easily eroded siltstone and shale of the Moenkopi Formation of Triassic age. The gently inclined slope on the east side of the valley is composed of the Virgin Limestone Member of the Moenkopi Formation.

15.2 Turnoff to Bonnie Springs Ranch on the left. It is the only commercial private land near the Red Rock Canyon National Conservation Area.

Wild burros are commonly seen along this route. They are not indigenous to this area, but are descendants of domesticated burros that were abandoned or escaped from their owners during the early mining days. The burros are protected by a 1971 law administered by the BLM. Please do not feed the burros.

Many springs and seeps occur at the base of the Wilson Cliffs. These issue water most voluminously during the spring and early

GEOLOGIC PERIOD		FORMATION SYMBOL	FORMATION NAME
Quaternary	1.6 Ma	Qa	Alluvial deposits
Tertiary (?)	66 Ma	Tbr	Landslide breccia
Cretaceous (?) and Jurassic		• • •	Brownstone Basin Conglomerate (conglomerate and sandstone)
Jurassic	205 Ma	Ja	Aztec Sandstone (red, tan or yellow cross-bedded sandstone)
Triassic		TRc	Chinle Formation and Shinarump Conglomerate (dark red to purple siltstone, mudstone, minor sandstone, and conglomerate)
	240 Ma	TRm	Moenkopi Formation (reddish siltstone, shale, and sandstone, with a prominent limestone member - the Virgin Limestone)
Permian		Pk	Kaibab (and Toroweap ?) Formations (gray limestone with intervals of white gypsum)
	290 Ma	Pr	Permian red beds (red sandstone and siltstone)
Pennsylvanian	330 Ma	IPb	Bird Spring Formation (gray limestone and dolostone)
Mississippian	360 Ma	Mm	Monte Cristo Limestone (gray limestone)
Devonian		Ds	Sultan Limestone (gray limestone) (unconformity, Silurian rocks missing)
Ordovician	500 Ma	Ou	Mountain Springs Formation and Pogonip (?) Group (dolostone and calcareous shale)
Cambrian		Ꞓn	Nopah Formation and Dunderberg Shale (dark gray shale and interbedded dolostone)
	570 Ma	Ꞓb	Bonanza King Formation (gray dolostone and limestone)

Ma = million years

Stratigraphic column for the Red Rock area (after Axen, 1984).

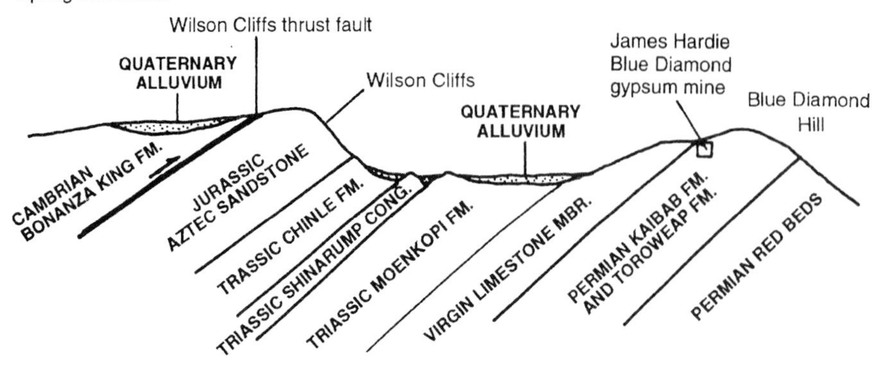

Generalized cross section looking south across Red Rock Valley.

summer; a few springs run year round. The springs are located at the base of the Wilson Cliffs because water and snowmelt that accumulate at higher elevations percolate downward into and through the permeable Aztec Sandstone. The rock layers that lie beneath the Aztec Sandstone at the base of the Wilson Cliffs belong to the Chinle Formation of Triassic age which is composed of shale and siltstone. There is very little pore space between the fine grains in siltstone and shale; therefore the Chinle Formation is far less permeable than the Aztec. Water that percolates through the Aztec eventually encounters the relatively impermeable Chinle layer and flows laterally until it encounters the ground surface—the face of the Wilson Cliffs. Here the water emerges as springs.

Burros at the entrance to Bonnie Springs Ranch.

A typical canyon east of the Wilson Cliffs surrounded by vegetation kept lush by springs. A similar photo in color is on the front cover.

15.9 The turnoff to Spring Mountain Ranch State Park is on the left. This area has a long history of use. An established campsite was reported by early travellers in the mid-1830s. It was an alternate route for pack and wagon trains on the Spanish/Fremont Trail which passed through Cottonwood Valley to the south (State Route 160). Use of this trail ceased with the establishment of the San Pedro, Los Angeles and Salt Lake Railroad in Las Vegas Valley in 1905. The ranch has had an interesting string of owners who used it as a working ranch and luxurious retreat. It was purchased by the Nevada Division of State Parks in 1974.

W
E
precipitation
water percolates through permeable sandstone
permeable Aztec Sandstone
water emerges in a spring
saturated
relatively impermeable Chinle Formation

How springs form in the Wilson Cliffs.

BLM Visitor Center.

16.6 First Creek trailhead on the left.

Red Rock Valley is in the Lower Sonoran life zone, known as the Mojave Desert. It hosts a large variety of plant life, including various types of yucca, Joshua tree yucca (a indicator plant of the Mojave Desert life zone), blackbrush, creosote bush, mesquite, catclaw, cholla, and many wildflowers. Nearer the Wilson Cliffs areas along streams and springs (riparian zones) support scrub oak, desert willow, redbud, Fremont cottonwood, and ash trees. The higher cliffs support vegetation of the Upper Sonoran life zone including pinyon pine, juniper, and ponderosa pine. In addition, more than 100 species of birds, 45 species of mammals, and 30 species of reptiles and amphibians live in the recreation area.

Joshua tree

17.1 The turnoff to Oak Creek is on the left.

18.6 Passing the end of the Red Rock Scenic Loop on the left. The colorful Calico Hills are straight ahead.

19.1 Red Rock Canyon Overlook and interpretive display on the left.

20.6 Turn left into the BLM Visitor Center and the entrance to the Red Rock scenic loop drive. Take this opportunity to visit the Visitor

Center (and bookstore) for fascinating and informative displays on the natural and human history of this area. You may also inquire about ranger-led interpretive tours in the area.

Leave the Visitor Center and back-track to the entrance of the Red Rock Scenic Loop Drive.

0.0 **Reset odometer to 0.0, turn left, and begin the 13-mile, one-way scenic drive through Red Rock.** (*Note:* the mileages include entering turnouts, parking areas, etc. where instructed.)

1.0 Calico Hills No. 1 Overlook on the right. Stop for a close-up view of the Aztec Sandstone. See color photo on front cover. This rock formation is present throughout much of the southwestern United States. In Zion National Park and the Lake Powell area of Utah this rock layer is called the Navajo Sandstone. In parts of Colorado and Utah, it is called the Nugget Formation. The widespread extent of this formation coupled with its distinctive compositional and depositional features allow geologists to infer the geological environment in which it was deposited with considerable confidence.

Cross-beds in Aztec Sandstone.

The sandstone is composed of well-rounded grains of almost pure quartz sand with no clay or silt. This observation indicates that the sand was deposited by some agent that was capable of removing fine material from the sediment and one that was efficient at rounding the edges of the sand grains by abrasion. Another diagnostic feature is the conspicuous cross stratification or cross-bedding. Unlike most sedimentary deposits that show planar stratification, the cliff in front of you shows multiple layers that are oriented at angles to one another. This type of stratification is a result of deposition by currents that were variable in direction and intensity. The large scale of individual cross-beds is most characteristic of deposition by wind currents.

The widespread extent of the Aztec Sandstone and its correlative formations throughout much of the southwestern United States suggests that this formation was deposited in a vast desert sand dune environment much like the present-day Sahara Desert.

Note that the sandstone varies in color from white or light tan to red. Note also that these color changes do not coincide with specific layers or beds within the sandstone, but appear to occur independently of layering. The ultimate origin of these color bands is not fully understood, but it probably involves the movement of groundwater through the rock after it was deposited. Upon prolonged exposure to oxygen and water in the subsurface, minerals that contain even small amounts of iron undergo oxidation, the same process that rusts metal. The result of this process is a red discoloration of the rock. Apparently, the lighter-colored areas somehow escaped oxidation; perhaps groundwater moved through the subsurface in an irregular fashion.

1.6 Calico Hills No. 2 Overlook on the right.

2.6 Sandstone Quarry to the right. Enter the parking area. One of the first industries established in the Las Vegas area after 1905 was this quarry which produced very hard (due to the presence of calcite or quartz cement between the sand grains) red and white sandstone for buildings in Las Vegas, Los Angeles, and San Francisco. A huge steam traction engine hauled the cut blocks to the railroad in Las Vegas. The quarry closed in 1912 due to competition from a new quarry closer to the railroad.

4.8 Scenic overlook on the left. A view to the south in Red Rock Valley reveals the gentle westward inclination of the strata on both sides of the valley. The valley developed by preferential erosion of the soft easily

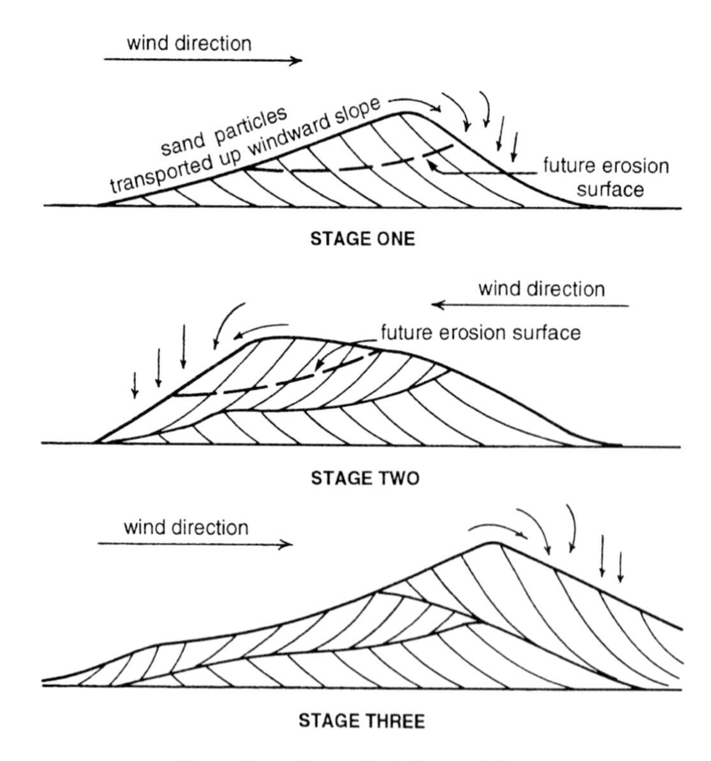

Formation of cross-beds in sandstone.

View looking south across the Red Rock Valley.

eroded shale and siltstone of the Moenkopi and Chinle Formations. The Wilson Cliffs rise above the valley floor because the Aztec Sandstone is far more resistant to erosion than the underlying layers.

The roadcuts on the right (north) side of the road show alluvial material eroded from the Wilson Cliffs and La Madre Mountain. Near the surface, the alluvium has been partially cemented by a white, impervious material called caliche. (Note the thin white lenses and coatings on pebbles.) Caliche is basically calcium carbonate, which

Caliche deposits in the Red Rock canyon area.

has been dissolved from the limestone and dolostone of the Spring Mountains, transported in surface and groundwater, and deposited (precipitated or crystallized) at depths of a few inches to several feet in voids below the land surface. Caliche also forms coatings on cobbles resting on the surface by capillary rise of calcium-rich groundwater. There is not enough precipitation in arid climates to wash the calcium minerals away. Thick, hard caliche deposits pose numerous problems for developers in arid regions. (Refer to page 85 for more information on caliche.)

6.0 **Turn off to White Rock Spring on the right. Drive up the road 1/2 mile.** Looking west, the abrupt termination of the Aztec Sandstone near the end of the road (near the trailhead to White Rock Spring) is due to a northwest-oriented, steeply inclined or nearly vertical fault named the La Madre fault. The block east of the fault has been dropped down relative to the block to the west, bringing the gray limestone of the older Bonanza King Formation (that lies above the Wilson Cliffs thrust fault) down against the younger tan Aztec Sandstone.

1. Older Bonanza King Formation is thrust over younger Aztec Sandstone.

2. La Madre fault cuts the rock units.

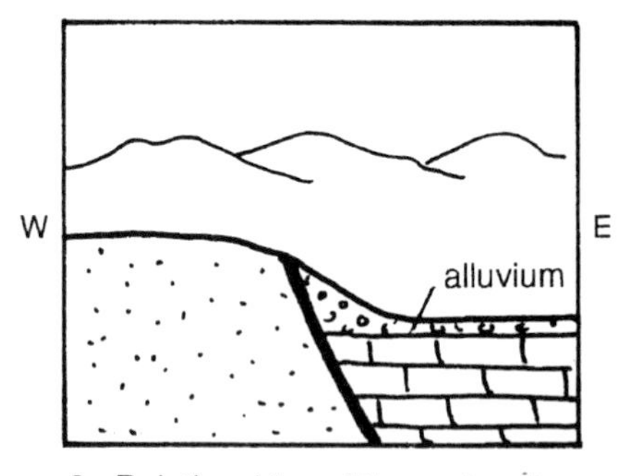

3. Relationships of the rocks after fault-block movement and erosion.

Geologic relationships at White Rock Spring.

7.6 More caliche deposits can be seen in the roadcuts to the right.

8.6 Turn right to the Willow Springs and Lost Creek picnic area (see color photo on page 21). Drive to the picnic area and **park**. Further travel is not recommended: the gravel road is passable to sedans for

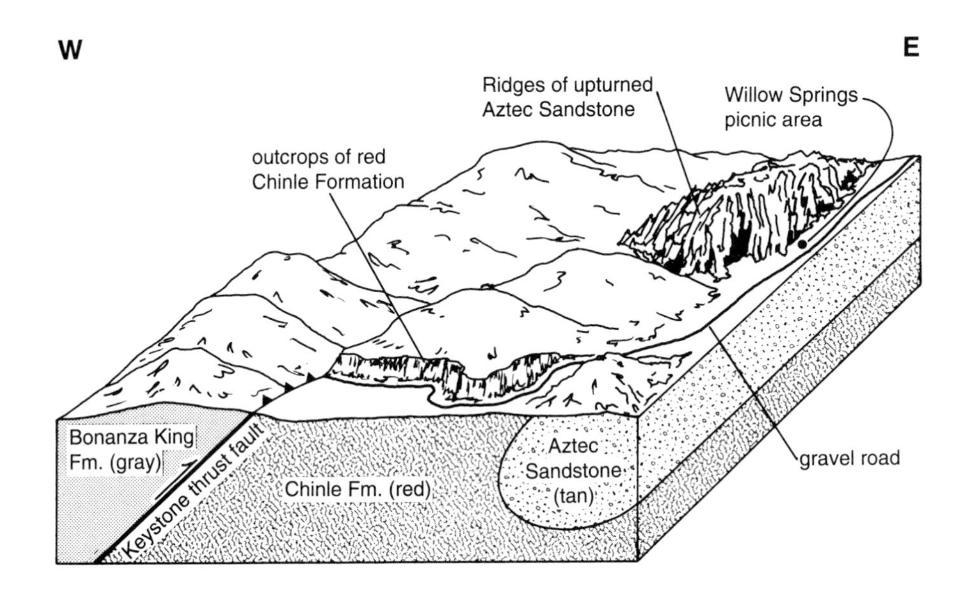

Geologic relationships just north of the Willow Springs picnic area.

another 1/2 mile but a high-axle or four-wheel drive vehicle is required beyond that point.

An **optional hike** west up the dirt road reveals interesting relationships beneath the major thrust fault in the Wilson Cliffs. Approximately 1/2 mile from the parking area, just beyond where the road crosses the stream bed, look to the right. The Aztec Sandstone is inclined very steeply downward toward Red Rock Valley (east). This orientation is opposite to the gentle west inclination of the strata back at the parking area. The Aztec Sandstone has been folded into a bowl-shaped configuration called a syncline.

Continuing up the road (**keep left** at the La Madre Springs Trail sign), the Aztec Sandstone ends and roadcuts now reveal dark red-brown siltstone and shale of the Chinle Formation that lies beneath the Aztec Sandstone. These layers have been tilted into a nearly vertical orientation. Continuing westward, the rocks become progressively older. The prominent gray cliffs to the north and west are gray limestone and dolostone of the Bonanza King Formation which are separated from the rocks here by the Keystone thrust fault.

This area also has numerous archeological sites. Along the cliffs are petroglyphs and agave pits attributed to the Anasazi culture (500 to 1150 A.D.) and southern Paiute Indians (1150 A.D. to recent time). Fossilized coral may be observed in the gray limestones and dolostones in the stream beds.

9.8 Return to the main loop road, turn right, and continue on. Note the dark patches of rock varnish coating the sandstone cliffs in this area. See page 94 for an explanation of rock varnish.

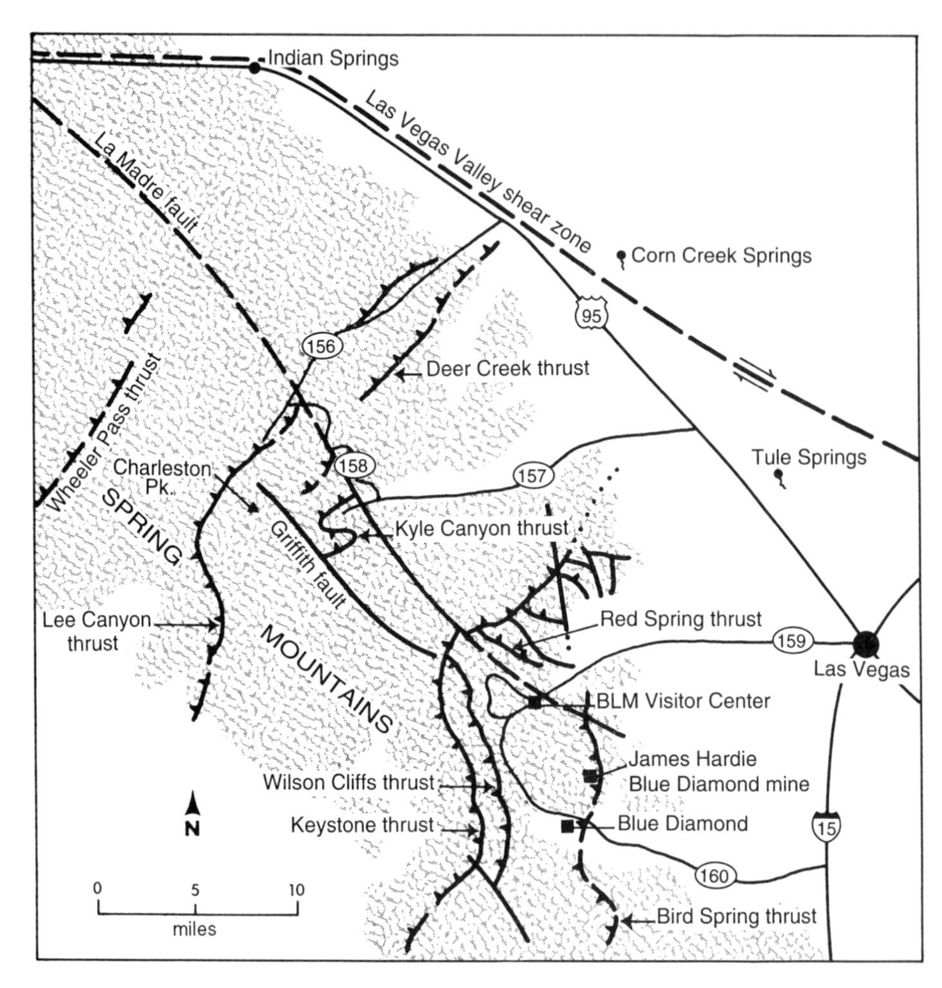

Major faults in the central and northern Spring Mountains (after Longwell and others, 1979).

10.4 Icebox Canyon trailhead on the right.

11.0 Crossing Red Rock Wash.

11.3 Red Rock Wash Overlook on the left.

13.0 Pine Creek Canyon Overlook and trailhead on the right. A fine example of Upper Sonoran vegetation may be observed here. Joshua trees of the Mojave Desert merge with pinyon and ponderosa pines, juniper, and aspen, and many varieties of shrubs.

14.4 Oak Creek trailhead to the right.

15.1 **End of Red Rock Canyon Scenic Loop Drive. Turn left onto State Route 159.**

17.1 Passing the entrance to the BLM Visitor Center. Return to Las Vegas via State Route 159 and Charleston Blvd.

18.7 Calico Basin Road on the left leads to the Red Rock picnic area (distance 1 mile). The Wilson Cliffs thrust fault (here it is called the Red Spring thrust for exposures near the Red Spring picnic area) appears as a sharp line separating the gray limestone of the Bonanza King Formation above, from the red Aztec Sandstone below (see color photo on back cover).

20.1 Leaving Red Rock Canyon National Conservation Area. Note that the road now parallels Red Rock Wash on the left. This is a flash flood area.

21.1 Red Rock Basin flood detention structure on the right. The Red Rock basin accumulates snowmelt and runoff from the Wilson Cliffs and La Madre Mountain. Spring snowmelt from these high areas is usually gradual enough that extremes of runoff resulting from snowmelt do not normally constitute a flood hazard. However, summer thunderstorms that build up over the Spring Mountains can produce large amounts of runoff in very short periods of time. As in many parts of the desert, flash floods are not uncommon in southern Nevada. Avoid parking and camping in dry creek beds.

Because the climb into Red Rock Valley from Las Vegas is so gradual, it is easy to overlook the fact that the floor of Red Rock Valley lies at an elevation of about 4,000 feet, nearly 2,000 feet higher than downtown Las Vegas. During heavy rains, runoff accumulates in the northern part of Red Rock Valley and is channeled through Red Rock Wash into Las Vegas Valley. The Red Rock basin flood detention structure was designed to prevent floodwater from reaching the city of Las Vegas.

Las Vegas has a long history of major floods due to brief, but intense summer rains. Much of the city is built in low-lying areas such as washes or floodplains of washes. These are natural courses for runoff. The process of urbanization itself further exacerbates the flood hazard. Since paved surfaces are impermeable to water, water simply runs off and accumulates in the low places rather than infiltrating into the ground. Because of the relatively infrequent heavy rains in the Las Vegas area, city leaders and developers must make a choice between spending huge sums of money for flood detention structures before construction on buildings can begin or opt for the lower costs of repairing damage after occasional flooding.

23.0 Entering Las Vegas on Charleston Boulevard. Directly east of the city are the two peaks of Sunrise Mountain (low, at 11:00) and Frenchman Mountain (high, at 12:00). These small mountain ranges are described in Trip 3.

View of Las Vegas and Frenchman Mountain looking east from Red Rock Valley.

Trip 2—Tule Springs and the Spring Mountains

This trip begins in northwest Las Vegas. The first stop takes you to Tule Springs, a refreshing spot in the northwestern part of Las Vegas Valley where several spring-fed pools are surrounded by tall shade trees. Archeologic and geologic highlights include some of the earliest evidence of humans in Las Vegas Valley, remains of Pleistocene megafauna including camels, mammoths, jaguars, horses, sloths, and bison, and,recent erosion of sediments that were deposited during the Ice Ages when the area was much wetter than it is today. Springs like this one provide water for a wide variety of native and introduced plants. Along the hike and bike trails are signs with the names of various planted trees and shrubs. Among the native desert plants found here are banana yucca, Mojave yucca, Mojave thistle, creosote bush, paperbag bush, indigo bush, buckhorn cholla, strawberry hedgehog cactus, beavertail cactus, spiny menodora, Mormon tea, and catclaw. Russian thistle, oleander, tamarisk (salt cedar), and cottonwood were introduced by man. Fish in the spring pools include rainbow trout and channel catfish.

From there, this route continues north on U.S. 95 to the Kyle Canyon turnoff (State Route 157) to the Spring Mountains. The trip proceeds up

A pond at Tule Springs, with the Las Vegas Range in the background (see page 21 for color).

Kyle Canyon, crosses over to Lee Canyon via State Route 158, and, after a visit to the Lee Canyon ski area, continues down Lee Canyon on State Route 156 to U.S. 95. The trip ends at the Desert Wildlife National Range Refuge and Corn Springs Flat on U.S. 95. This trip, if taken in its entirety, will cover nearly 100 miles. Be sure that you have enough gasoline before you start. **No gasoline is available in the Spring Mountains**.

0.0 Begin at the intersection of Rancho Drive (Tonopah Highway, Business 95) and U.S. 95. **Set your odometer to 0.0 and drive northwest on U.S. 95**.

0.7 The Spring Mountains are to the left (at 9:00). The Sheep Range is at 1:00, and the Las Vegas Range is at 3:00.

3.1 Turn right onto Durango Drive toward Floyd Lamb State Park. The Sheep Range is straight ahead.

4.6 Turn right toward the State Park.

5.1 Stop at the park, which is built around Tule Springs. The mounds of white calcareous mudstones were deposited in a pluvial (from the Latin *pluvia*, rain) lake that formed here from about 30,000 to 15,000 years ago during the early and middle Pleistocene glacial epoch. Las Vegas Valley was drained by a sizable stream during this time which flowed into Las Vegas Wash, as it does today. The dynamics of this drainage system are strikingly different today, however, because of the change in climate and the impact of human development in the valley. Las Vegas Wash is visited in Trip 4.

Thick Pleistocene deposits formed by ancient Tule Springs Lake.

Between about 15,000 and 9,000 years ago, this area alternated between stream and marsh environments. The geologic history of this area is very similar to that of the Corn Springs Flat area to the north which is visited at the end of this trip.

From 32,000 to 11,000 years ago, the Tule Springs area was inhabited by a variety of animals resembling the wildlife of East Africa today. Fossilized remains of large animals including camels, mammoths, jaguars, horses, sloths, and bison have been found in the sediments here. They became extinct about 11,000 years ago in southern Nevada and throughout North America—about the same time that manmade stone projectile points are recorded in the archeological record in North America.

Man was firmly established in North America about 11,500 years ago. Other locations, such as the Lehner site in southern Arizona, have yielded stone projectile points along with bones at mammoth kill sites. Here at Tule Springs, scientists also hoped to find evidence of man along with the animals when, in 1962, they excavated and sifted through 200,000 tons of earth along the shore of ancient Tule Springs Lake. Their goal was to positively determine the presence of humans here as early as 28,000 years ago, but the study was inconclusive.

Return to the Durango and U.S. 95 intersection. Reset odometer to 0.0. Turn right on U.S. 95. Proceed north to the Spring Mountains via the Kyle Canyon Road (State Route 157).

The Spring Mountains offer both winter and summer recreation. In the summer, temperatures are 20° to 25°F cooler than in Las Vegas and the pine and fir forest provides a welcome relief from the heat for the hiker, picnicker, or cyclist. A small ski area, Lee Canyon, affords winter recreation less than an hour from downtown Las Vegas.

It has long been recognized that increased elevation produces climatic changes that are similar to those that occur with increased latitude (toward the poles of the Earth). The different climatic zones encountered as one goes up in elevation or travels northward (in the northern hemisphere) result in notable differences in vegetation type. Plant ecologists recognize six different vegetation associations or life zones in this area. The 10,000-foot ascent from Las Vegas to the summit of Charleston Peak is equivalent, in terms of vegetation associations, to a trip from Las Vegas to the Canadian arctic. The four life zones encountered on the road up Kyle Canyon will be discussed in this trip guide. The upper two life zones are only encountered on a hike to the top of Charleston Peak.

The Spring Mountains record an impressive geological event—the compressive mountain-building episode called the Sevier Orogeny. About 100 to 70 million years ago, 500 to 400 million-year-old, gray dolostones (sedimentary rocks composed of the mineral dolomite, calcium-magnesium carbonate) were thrusted or pushed on top of 180 to 170 million-year-old red sandstones.

Later, these rocks were broken apart by normal faults making the picture today very complex to unravel. The route follows and crosses some of the major thrust faults in the range.

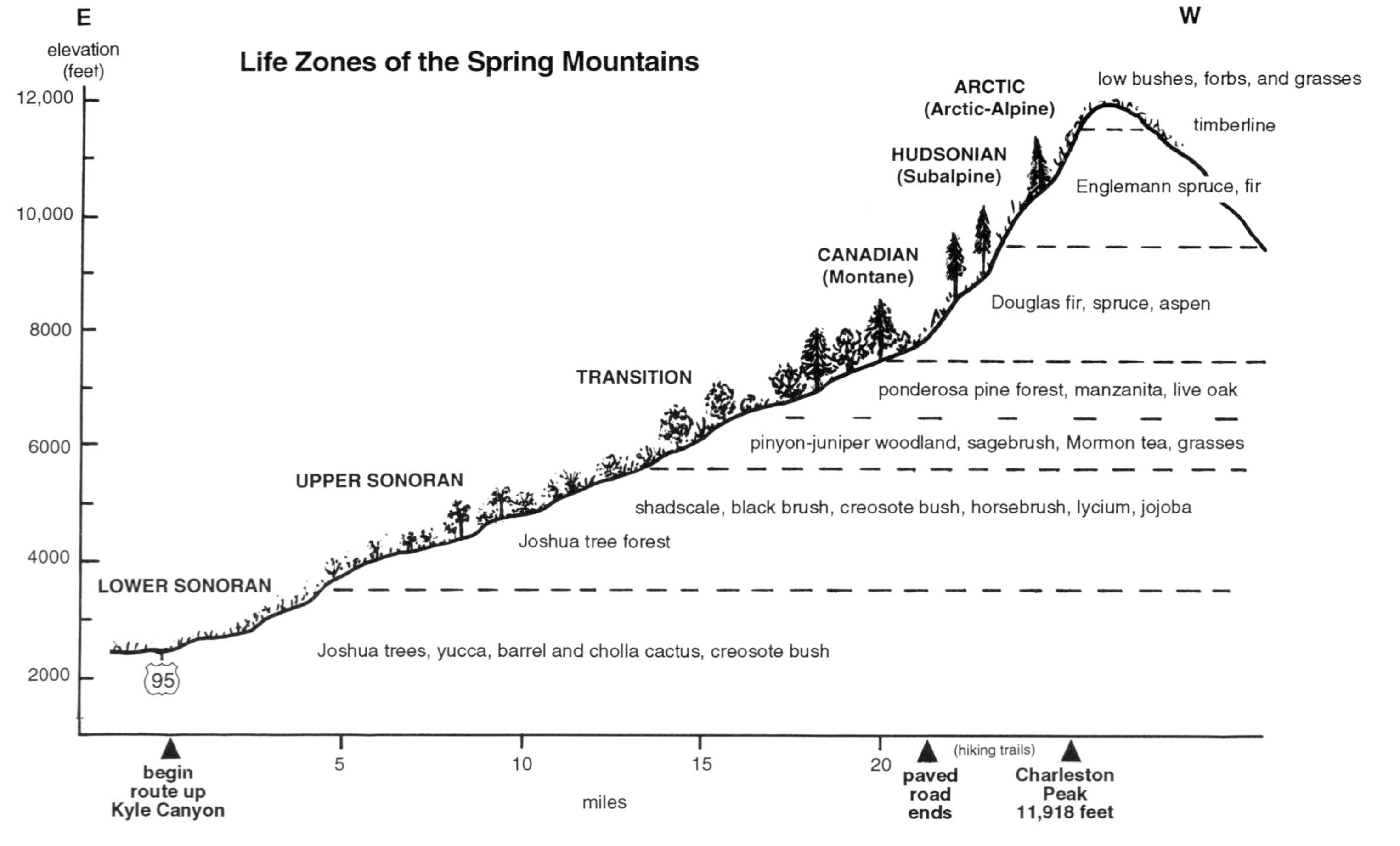

Life zones in the Spring Mountains.

3.1 **Turn left to Mount Charleston via Kyle Canyon Road. Reset odometer to 0.0.**

The route is within the Lower Sonoran life zone, typical of most desert areas below about 3,500 feet above sea level. The scant 4 inches of average annual precipitation that falls on the Las Vegas Valley permits the growth of only the most hardy plants—creosote bush, blackbrush, yucca, agave, mesquite, ephedra (Mormon tea), and various cactus species.

Plants of the Lower Sonoran life zone along Kyle Canyon.

Joshua tree forest. Joshua tree yucca are members of the lily family and occur naturally only in the Mojave Desert of the southwestern United States.

Vegetation of the Upper Sonoran life zone in Kyle Canyon.

4.3 Ahead on the left, the smaller hill at 11:00 is composed of well-stratified limestone and dolostone of the Pennsylvanian-Permian Bird Spring Formation. The larger hill at 10:00 is made up of Monte Cristo Limestone of Mississippian age. These latter rocks are equivalent in age to the prominent cliff-forming Redwall Limestone in the Grand Canyon. This limestone formed in shallow, warm oceans and contains fossils common to the Mississippian time period. The topographic slope is parallel to, and governed by, the inclination (dip) of the rock layers. Geologists refer to this as a dip slope.

7.0 For the next few miles, the route passes through a Joshua tree forest. Between about 3,500 and 5,500 feet above sea level, precipitation is sufficient to support the more varied vegetation of the Upper Sonoran zone. This zone is typified by the dominance of sagebrush, shadscale, saltbush (in saline soils), and, in the Mojave Desert of the southwestern United States, Joshua trees. Many plants from the Lower Sonoran zone persist into the Upper Sonoran zone. Rocks on both sides of the road are the Bird Spring Formation.

The prominent white area at 9:00 high on the ridge is a relatively fresh landslide scar. During the landslide, a large slab of rock failed abruptly along a bedding surface which functioned as a zone of weakness. This type of slope failure is referred to as a block slide. Gray, angular, limestone rubble—the actual landslide deposit—is evident below the landslide scar.

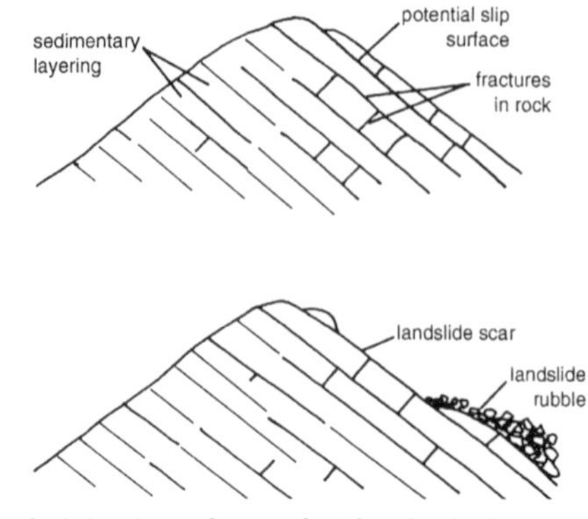

Block slide along the south side of Kyle Canyon.

This landslide serves as an example that erosion in steep mountainous areas is not always a slow and gradual process, but may be quite sudden and catastrophic.

8.8 The route now descends into Kyle Canyon wash. Deposits of the Pleistocene (1,500,000 to 10,000 years ago) Kyle Canyon alluvial fan are evident above the road. The Kyle Canyon alluvial fan—actually composed of six distinct alluvial fan deposits—represents large aprons of debris that were shed off the high Spring Mountains in stream drainages and deposited near the lower reaches of the range. The modern-day drainage system has cut down into these earlier alluvial fan deposits exposing their internal stratigraphy (layering). The large amount of debris represented by the Kyle Canyon alluvial fan dwarfs the volume of material that is presently being eroded from the Spring Mountains. This difference in intensity of erosion and the size of the resultant alluvial deposit is probably due to climate change. Analysis of fossil plant material indicates that precipitation in southern Nevada was much greater during the Pleistocene Epoch (Ice Age) than at present.

Aerial view looking northwest. Eroded deposits of the Kyle Canyon fan are in the center of the photo. Charleston Peak is in the upper left corner of the photo.

The bouldery layers exposed in Las Vegas Wash at the Northshore Road bridge (refer to Trip 4) are probably correlative with the bouldery layers of the Kyle Canyon fan.

9.6 Just ahead on the right, tan Kyle Canyon fan material is plastered against gray bedrock of the Bird Spring Formation, composed mainly of limestone.

9.9 Folds within the Bird Spring Formation are evident to the left (south) of the road. To the east, the layers are inclined (dip) to the northeast. To the west, the layers dip northwest. This folding is related to the major phase of compressional deformation that occurred during the Cretaceous Period. This major mountain building event is discussed in the introduction.

10.4 The Kyle Canyon alluvial fan is composed of boulders, cobbles, pebbles, and sand eroded from the Spring Mountains. The crudely

Pleistocene age alluvial fan material plastered against bedrock exposed in Kyle Canyon.

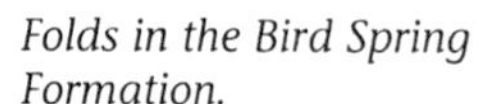

Folds in the Bird Spring Formation.

defined and irregular layering within the fan deposit is typical of material carried by debris flows or mudflows. These types of deposits involve minor amounts of water relative to the amount of sediment—just enough to move rock, sand, and mud material as a thick, sticky mass. In contrast, normal river deposits, which involve large amounts of water relative to the amount of sediment, show more defined and even stratification (layering) as well as more uniform size material. The larger, heavier pebbles will settle to the bottom of the stream deposit first and the sediments get finer toward the top of the deposit because they are lighter and are suspended longer in the water.

11.0 Isolated blocks and spires are parts of ancient fan deposits that simply have not yet been eroded away by the present-day Kyle Creek. The older deposits are heavily cemented with calcium (called calcrete) derived from the limestone rocks forming the bulk of the range. Calcrete is similar to the caliche seen on Trips 1 and 3, but is formed in the presence of more moisture, such as the bottom of stream beds and lakes that cyclicly fill and evaporate. These spires are held up by cemented, gravel-rich layers that are more resistant to erosion than the sediments that underlie them. Spires similar to these can be seen in Techatticup Wash (Eldorado Canyon) between Nelson and Lake Mead on Trip 4 (color photo on page 28).

An erosional remnant of Kyle Canyon alluvium showing graded bedding and differential erosion.

12.6 The turnoff to Harris Spring Road is on the left. The route enters the Transition zone which is marked by the rather abrupt appearance of pinyon and juniper trees. This plant association (informally called PJ) is common throughout the southwest. In many areas, one plant species will dominate over the other, however, here the two species are present in approximately equal amounts. The pinyons are the larger, dusty green trees with large needles and well-defined trunks. The junipers are bright olive green and more shrublike. Other vegetation types include rabbitbrush, sagebrush, wildflowers. Ponderosa pine, mountain mahogany, and oak dominate at the highest elevations of the Transition zone (6,500 to 7,000 feet).

Pinyon-juniper woodland of the Transition zone.

17.0 Charleston Hotel turnoff. Remnants of the tan and gray, cemented Kyle Canyon fan form cliffs behind the hotel (on the opposite side of the drainage). Deposits are plastered against the nearly horizontal layers of Paleozoic limestone.

17.2 The active channel of Kyle Creek is on the left. Large boulders provide evidence of erosion and transport of coarse alluvial material during flooding. One reason that the creeks in the Spring Mountains flow so infrequently is that the limestone and dolostone that compose most of the range are highly fractured and contain numerous cavities formed due to dissolution (dissolving) of the limestone. Hence, most of the drainage is in the subsurface.

This relatively open area marks the intersection of at least three faults.

17.6 The Lee Canyon turnoff (State Route 158) is on the right. **Continue straight ahead** through a ponderosa (yellow) pine and oak forest that marks the uppermost levels of the Transition zone. Between this point and the Kyle Canyon ranger station ahead, the road is parallel to the trace of the Kyle Canyon thrust fault and crosses it twice. Rocks on both sides of the fault are Permian-Pennsylvanian Bird Springs Formation.

18.0 Kyle Canyon Campground on the left. Charleston Peak (11,918 feet), the third highest mountain in Nevada, looms straight ahead.

18.2 Kyle Canyon Ranger Station on the left.

Ponderosa pine and oak forest characteristic of the upper levels of the Transition zone.

Aspen, Douglas fir, and spruce characteristic of the Canadian (or montane) life zone.

18.4 Fletcher View campground on the left.

19.0 The route passes through the "town" of Rainbow. This is an informal name given to a cluster of cabins. No services are available. The elevation here is about 7,300 feet above sea level. Scattered aspen, Douglas fir, and spruce signal that the route has entered the Canadian (or montane) life zone. This is the highest life zone encountered along the road.

A hike to the summit of Charleston Peak via either the North Rim Trail or the South Rim Trail (consult U.S. Forest Service maps) will take you through the Hudsonian (or Subalpine) zone dominated by Englemann spruce, and various species of fir. The Arctic (or Arctic-Alpine) zone begins at timberline. It is equivalent to Arctic tundra and is characterized by lack of tree species and domination by low plants.

20.0 Old Town. No services available.

20.3 Note the older Kyle Canyon fan deposits on the right.

20.5 Hairpin turn left to Cathedral Rock. For access to several trailheads, continue straight for less than a mile on "Echo Road." Cabins are on the right, and aspens are on the left.

21.0 "Y" intersection in road. The gravel road on the right leads to the trailhead for the South Rim trail (0.3 mile) from this intersection. This trail provides access to Charleston Peak and the Deer Creek area.

View looking west from the parking area of Mount Charleston Lodge. The valley is bounded by high cliffs formed of Mississippian limestones which are cut off by the nearly vertical Griffith fault.

The left fork continues for 0.2 mile where it ends at Mount Charleston Lodge. From here one can hike to Mary Jane Falls and Big Falls. Maps and information regarding the trails are available from the U.S. Forest Service office in Kyle Canyon (open between May 1 and September 30) or in Las Vegas. These are short hikes (1 to 2 miles each way), but become steeper toward the end. The hike to Big Falls involves hiking up boulders in a stream bed. Despite their modest distances, these hikes should not be undertaken without Forest Service maps and adequate footwear. The rocks that you will encounter on these hikes are part of the Mississippian Monte Cristo Limestone and the Devonian Sultan Formation. Because the rocks in this part of the Spring Mountains are only gently tilted, the rock layers become younger as one climbs upward. The rocks at the top of Charleston Peak belong to the Bird Spring Formation. This stratigraphic unit makes up most of the exposures along the south rim of Kyle Canyon.

From the Mount Charleston Lodge parking area, look west. The valley is bounded by a line of high cliffs formed of Mississippian limestones. They are cut off by the nearly vertical Griffith fault.

Alluvial fan deposits of the Kyle Canyon fan are exposed in the roadcuts to the Cathedral Rock Picnic Area, located near the lodge, indicating that the present-day canyon was choked with fan debris at least this far up the mountain. The present-day drainage of Kyle Creek has cut through (dissected) these deposits.

Retrace route back down the mountain on the main road.

Below the Cathedral Rock Picnic Ground, notice that the rocks on the north side (left) of the canyon are tilted in various directions. A series of faults associated with the Deer Creek thrust fault (to be observed later) cut across the road just east of the hairpin turn. These faults place various rock layers against one another in a complex fashion. Deformation of the layers associated with movement along these faults has resulted in the variable and chaotic tilting of the strata at this locality. See page 42 for a map of faults in this area.

Turn left (north) on State Route 158 (Deer Creek Road) and reset odometer to 0.0.

1.0 La Madre Mountain can be seen at 2:00 to 3:00. This view is toward the north side of the mountain. The rocks that make up the north side of La Madre Mountain lie in the upper plate of the Keystone thrust and have been folded into a large syncline (refer to the lower figure on page 14). The core of the syncline is the Triassic Moenkopi Formation. The winding route is on the Bird Spring Formation.

1.9 Roadcuts expose more Kyle Canyon fan debris. The trace of the northwest-trending La Madre fault lies parallel to and just below road level on the right for about the next 2 miles.

3.1 On the north and east slopes (left side of road), vegetation zones are conspicuously mixed. Ponderosa pine, spruce, and a few aspen of the Transition-Canadian zone occur in the protected and sheltered areas such as drainage areas. On more exposed slopes, pinyon and juniper of the lower Transition zone predominate. The difference in vegetation types here is not due to elevation alone, but also to microenvironmental factors such as degree of exposure to the sun, moisture retention properties of the soil, and depth of the soil. Much intermixing of vegetation types occurs in transitional areas.

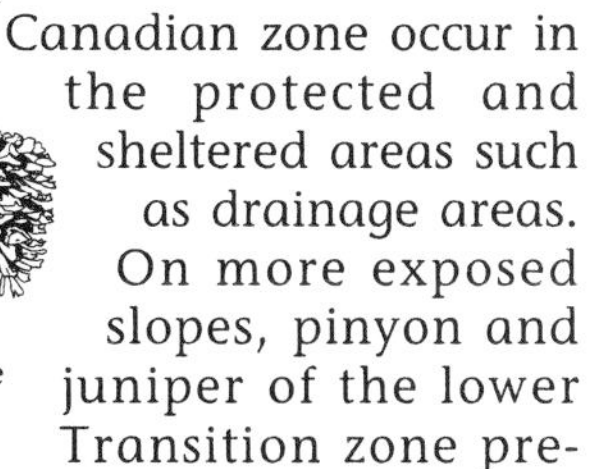

Ponderosa pine

Roadcuts along State Route 158 exposing Kyle Canyon fan debris. Note the large boulder in the center of the photo.

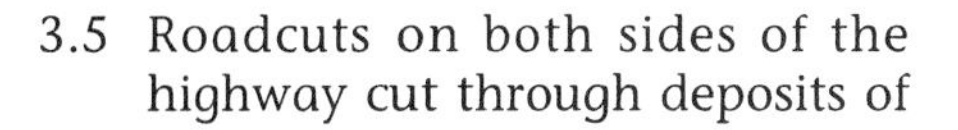

3.5 Roadcuts on both sides of the highway cut through deposits of

Mummy Mountain and vegetation characteristic of the Canadian life zone.

the Kyle Canyon fan. Note that individual boulders, or clasts, locally exceed 2 feet in diameter. These large blocks reflect the proximity of the fan deposit to its source—the high Spring Mountains.

4.5 The turnoff to Hilltop (SMYC sign) Campground is on the right. The prominent mountain directly ahead (west) is Mummy Mountain, composed mostly of Devonian and Mississippian formations. At an elevation of over 11,400 feet, it is not uncommon for snow to persist on this mountain until early June. Its profile, nearly 3 miles long, is very similar to a person lying down.

5.3 Mahogany Grove group picnic area on the right. The road to Deer Creek Spring is to the left.

5.5 Deer Creek picnic area parking lot on the right. **Park car** and examine the rocks that have been caught up in the Deer Creek thrust fault zone. This fault is part of the Keystone thrust system that is described in Trip 1. At this location, the fault places rocks of the Cambrian Bonanza King Formation over younger Mississippian Monte Cristo Limestone. Movement along the fault occurred as a result of compressive forces in the Earth's crust that occurred between 100 and 70 million years ago, a geological event called the Sevier Orogeny.

Roadcuts on both sides of road expose highly sheared limestones that have been caught up in the fault zone. Movement along the Deer Creek thrust fault resulted in crushing and grinding of rock into angular fragments (fault breccia) and rock powder (fault gouge). On

Deer Creek thrust fault zone on the north (left) side of the parking area. Plants are about 3 feet high.

Close-up view of slickensides on the fault surface in the Deer Creek thrust fault zone (north side of the parking area).

the south (right) side of the road, the rocks have been completely overturned and overridden by the thrust plate.

On the north (left) side of the road, note the brecciated rocks that contain highly polished and reflective surfaces that have been produced by abrasive action during movement along the fault. Such polished and grooved surfaces are called slickensides. The orientation of the grooves on the slickenside surface provides geologists with important clues regarding the direction of movement (horizontal, vertical, or oblique) along the fault surface.

6.3 Dark gray Paleozoic limestone is exposed in the roadcut. Nearby roadcuts at approximately the same elevation expose rocks of the Pleistocene Kyle Canyon alluvial fan. This observation indicates that an irregular topographic surface existed at the time of deposition of the Kyle Canyon fan. As the fan debris was shed off of the Spring Mountains, it first filled existing valleys and other low-lying areas. These valleys were separated by ridges or divides composed of the limestone bedrock. As deposition of the fan material continued, many of these divides were eventually buried beneath fan debris.

The former high-standing ridges and divides of limestone are evident in roadcuts where Paleozoic limestone is exposed. A modern-day example of this type of ridge and valley topography can be seen below the intersection of the Lee Canyon and Deer Creek roads.

7.3 Desert Viewpoint on the right (see photo on page 22). The white color of the limestone at the far end of the large roadcut is due to bleaching (mineralogical and chemical changes) related to intense faulting of the limestone in this area. Below this stop, the Desert View Natural Environment Area extends out on the dry alluvial fans to U.S. 95. The Desert National Wildlife Range extends along the east side of U.S. 95, encompassing six major mountain ranges including the Sheep and Las Vegas Ranges from Indian Springs on the north to Las Vegas on the south—almost 1.5 million acres. It was created in 1936 and is the largest wildlife refuge in the contiguous United States. Its most important objective is to perpetuate the desert bighorn sheep and its habitat and it has the single largest concentration of these sheep in the country.

7.6 Mummy Mountain is straight ahead.

7.9 Mountain mahogany is abundant on both sides of the road.

8.9 Intersection with State Route 156 (Lee Canyon Road). **Turn left to Lee Canyon Ski Area**. Lee Canyon is formed in the trace of a major thrust fault for most of its length.

10.7 Old Mill picnic area.

10.9 Lee Canyon meadow. There is not another mountain meadow for more than 150 miles in any direction.

11.5 McWilliams Campground to the right. Campgrounds in the Spring Mountains area are generally open from May 1 to September 1. Reservations may be required on weekends and holidays.

11.7 Dolomite Campground to the right.

12.1 The road ends at the Lee Canyon ski area. Turn around and descend the mountain on the Lee Canyon road. **Reset odometer to 0.0 at the intersection of Lee Canyon road (State Route 156) and Deer Creek Road (State Route 158)**.

0.0 Continue straight ahead on the Lee Canyon Road (State Route 156).

8.7 Leaving Spring Mountains National Recreation Area.

9.0 The low hills ahead on the right (south) side of road display contorted and folded limestones of the Bird Spring Formation (refer to the figure on page 14 for types of folds). The Sheep Range, with a maximum elevation of 9,912 feet at Hayford Peak, is at 10:00-11:00. Note the large alluvial fans at the base of the range. The Black Hills (small range just west of the Sheep Range) are nearly completely buried by the alluvial debris shed off the Sheep Range (refer to page 121 for a sketch of landforms typical in the arid Basin and Range province).

11.2 Note the playa (dry lake bed) at the south end of Three Lakes Valley in the distance. The rock strata of all mountain ranges visible to the north are tilted to the east at angles that range from 40° to 70°. These ranges were formed during Basin and Range extension (from about 20 to 8 million years ago in this area). Much of southern Nevada was moved westward relative to the stable Colorado Plateau during this major deformational event and the rocks of many mountains ranges were tilted to the east by movement along faults that were inclined to the west.

14.2 Intersection with U.S. 95. **Turn right to Las Vegas.**

17.0 The Lee Canyon thrust fault lies within the prominent hill at about 3:00. The steeply northwest dipping (actually overturned) strata of the Bird Spring Formation have been thrust over gently northwest tilted strata of the same formation. The thrust occurs at the boundary or contact between these differently oriented strata.

To the left of the highway, and located at the foot of the Kyle Canyon alluvial fan, are thick white sediments of Corn Creek Flat. These are Pleistocene shallow lake deposits (calcareous mudstones) from Corn Creek Springs Lake which existed between 30,000 and 15,000 years ago. This ancient lake was the head of Las Vegas Creek, merging with the Tule Springs lake-marsh-stream area visited at the beginning of this trip.

Lee Canyon ski area and vegetation characteristic of the Hudsonian life zone.

Thick, light-colored Pleistocene lake deposits of Corn Creek Flat.

18.6 Entering the Desert View Natural Environment area. Turn left to Corn Creek Springs (a distance of about 3 miles) and the Desert National Wildlife Range refuge field station. One can view displays at the visitor center which provide an excellent introduction to the wildlife of the area, enjoy the lush vegetation around the springs, and perhaps see bighorn sheep at the field station.

In this area, mounds of soft lake sediments have been blown into dunes and later stabilized by shrubs and grasses.

Return to Las Vegas via U.S. 95.

Aerial view looking north over the white calcareous mudstone deposits of Pleistocene Corn Creek Springs Lake.

Trip 3—Frenchman Mountain and Valley of Fire

This trip runs east from Las Vegas, through Frenchman Mountain, and along Northshore Road north of Lake Mead. The trip culminates in a visit to the Valley of Fire before completing the loop back to Las Vegas via I-15. The total mileage of the trip is about 120 miles. Gasoline is available at Overton, 60 miles from Las Vegas, and at the intersection of State Route 169 with I-15.

The stretch of road along the north shore of Lake Mead is one of the most scenically spectacular and geologically complex in the southwestern United States. Just east of here the Basin and Range province on the north and west meets the Colorado Plateau to the east. The rocks tell a story of how the two provinces, a single geologic entity during long periods of deposition and erosion in a variety of Paleozoic and Mesozoic environments, were separated structurally by extensional forces during the Cenozoic Era.

Frenchman Mountain, looking east from North Las Vegas.

During this trip you will see some effects of the extensional deformation that mainly occurred 17 to 10 million years ago. (1) Entire mountains that were clearly once situated much further east have been displaced westward along faults. The rocks of Frenchman Mountain, directly east of Las Vegas, have been correlated with identical rocks situated east of Lake Mead. In addition, the Spring Mountains contain unique structures that indicate that they once formed a continuous geologic block with the Muddy Mountains north of Lake Mead. Some geologists believe that Frenchman Mountain and the Spring Mountains have been moved to the west along major faults. (2) Rock layers have been highly tilted, folded, and broken by faults as this region was pulled apart. (3) Much volcanic activity accompanied this period of crustal extension. As the Earth's crust was pulled apart, magma (molten rock) welled up and was expelled through vents and fissures in the Earth's crust to form lava flows and volcanoes.

0.0 The trip starts at the intersection of Lake Mead Boulevard (State Route 147) and Hollywood Boulevard in North Las Vegas. **Set odometer to 0.0 and proceed east on Lake Mead Boulevard.**

Looming ahead and on your right is Frenchman Mountain; the lower hills to the left (north) of the road are part of Sunrise Mountain. The rocks in Frenchman Mountain range in age from 1.7 billion years (Precambrian) to as young as 5 million years (Miocene).

The Precambrian rocks occur on the west side of the mountain at its base; the youngest rocks are on the east side of the mountain.

Aerial view looking southwest. Sunrise Mountain is in the foreground, Frenchman Mountain is in the middle, and Las Vegas Valley is in the background. Lake Mead Boulevard runs east-west between the two mountains.

Frenchman Mountain.

Although there are some major gaps, the long time span represented by these rocks affords the most complete record available of the geologic history of this part of Nevada during the past 1.7 billion years.

The sequence of Paleozoic rocks exposed on Frenchman Mountain is different from the rocks of the same age in other mountainous areas that surround the Las Vegas Valley, but is very similar to those

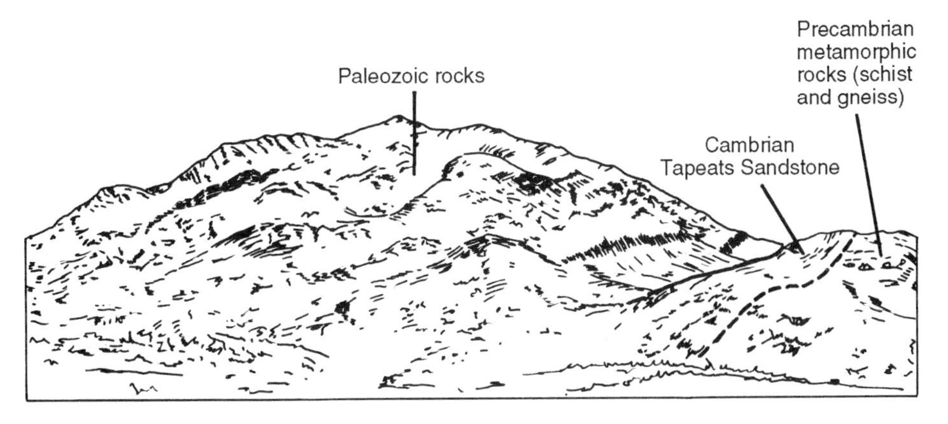

General stratigraphic units exposed on Frenchman Mountain at mile 1.1. The dashed line is the boundary between Precambrian and Cambrian rocks (after Rowland, 1987).

exposed in the western part of the Grand Canyon, more than 60 miles to the east. Similarity in the thickness and rock type of individual formations on Frenchman Mountain and in the western Grand Canyon, coupled with unique deposits in Tertiary rocks on the east side of Frenchman Mountain, led Chester Longwell to propose that Frenchman Mountain was once located near the present east end of Lake Mead. Longwell presented geological evidence that suggested that Frenchman Mountain was shifted to its present position during Cenozoic time along the Las Vegas Valley shear zone, a major right-lateral strike-slip fault that lies along the northern margin of Las Vegas Valley. Currently, most geologists agree that Frenchman Mountain is "out-of-place" and originated far to the east of its present location, but considerable controversy exists among geologists regarding the exact original position of the mountain, the faults that caused movement of the block, and the period of time in which this movement occurred.

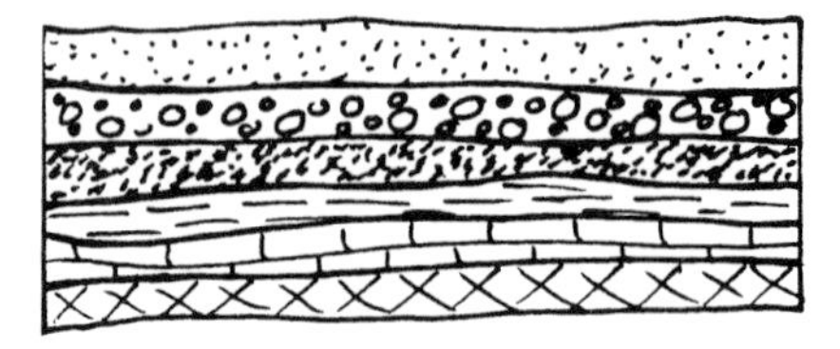

1. Deposition of sediments, which are consolidated into sedimentary rocks.

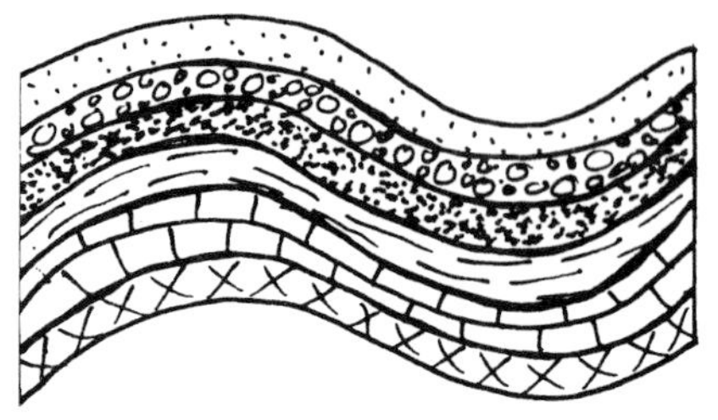

2. Tilting or folding of sedimentary rocks during uplift.

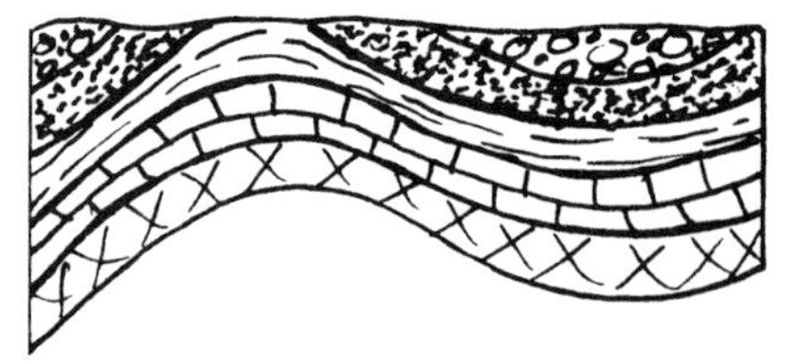

3. Erosion of deformed sedimentary rocks produce "gap" in geologic record.

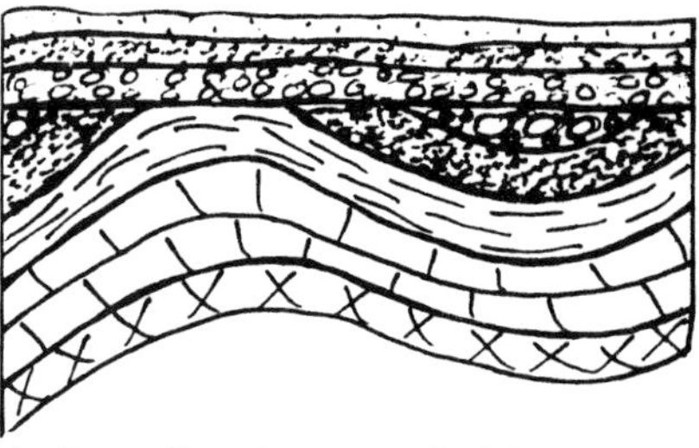

4. Deposition of younger, flat-lying sediments on older deformed sedimentary rocks.

Formation of unconformities.

0.9 Rocks immediately to the right (south) of the road are Precambrian igneous and metamorphic rocks that are similar to the 1.7 billion-year-old rocks found in the inner gorge of the Grand Canyon. Resting on the Precambrian rocks are conspicuously layered, brown rocks that are tilted to the east. These layered rocks are part of the Cambrian Tapeats Sandstone (about 520 million years old). Thus, there is a gap of more than 1 billion years in the geologic record between the Precambrian and Cambrian rocks at this locality. If rocks were deposited during this time interval, they must have been removed by erosion prior to the deposition of the Tapeats Sandstone, for we find no trace of them in southern Nevada.

This situation, where rocks are removed by erosion, creates a gap in the geologic record and is called an unconformity.

Optional hike to examine the different rock types and the Precambrian-Cambrian boundary. Walk south across the dry wash to the base of the hill. Then, walk eastward along the base of the hill for about 0.1 mile. Stop at the small, flat mound littered with broken glass. The contact between Precambrian gneiss and schist (right) and Cambrian sandstone (left) can be seen in the cut above this area. A zone of soft, tan weathered soil marks the time gap between the two very different rock types.

The Precambrian metamorphic rocks here are mostly biotite (black mica) schist and banded gneiss composed mainly of feldspar, biotite, and quartz. Some samples of gneiss contain crystals of red garnet. Plutonic rocks include granite and pegmatite.

Pegmatite is essentially granite with extremely large crystals which grew in pockets and veins by slow precipitation from gaseous fluids. Locally, the pegmatite contains large crystals of the mineral microcline. Most of the pieces on the ground are cleavage fragments that have been broken from even larger single crystals.

The overlying Cambrian Tapeats Sandstone consists of thin cross-beds (refer to Trip 1 for an explanation of cross-beds) of sand which host numerous fossilized worm trails, burrows, and grazing patterns indicating that this was a marine beach environment during the time of deposition. You may continue hiking east to observe more

Photograph of the contact between Precambrian metamorphic and igneous rocks and overlying, tilted sandstone of the Cambrian Period.

Paleozoic rocks, which are the oldest rocks that contain numerous fossils of animals with hard shells.

Return to your car and continue east on Lake Mead Boulevard. (You may already have hiked to the next mileage point.)

1.1 Notice that the rock layers on Frenchman Mountain are tilted to the east about 50°. This tilting resulted from the Cenozoic extension event discussed in the introduction and probably occurred as Frenchman Mountain was transported to the west from its original location. Because of the eastward tilt of strata, you will encounter successively younger rocks as you drive east through the pass on Frenchman Mountain.

The road through Frenchman Mountain coincides approximately with the trace of the Frenchman fault. This is a normal fault in which rocks of Sunrise Mountain have dropped down in relation to those of Frenchman Mountain. For this reason, the rocks on the north (left) side of the road (mainly Permian Kaibab Formation) are younger than the rocks at similar elevations on the south (right) side (mainly Cambrian through Mississippian rocks).

Desert plants in this area include creosote bush, skeleton weed, desert trumpet, Mormon tea, mesquite, Kearney's buckwheat, and desert seepweed.

2.6 To the left of the road, the rock layers are no longer tilted east but have been bent around to a more southerly tilt. This bending, very apparent from the air, is probably a consequence of movement along a major strike-slip fault, the Las Vegas Valley shear zone, which lies north of Sunrise Mountains. Strike-slip faults form where two crustal blocks slide horizontally past one another. The San Andreas fault of California is a well-known example of a strike-slip fault.

3.7 Bright-red Aztec Sandstone crops out directly south of the road at 3:00. This is the same rock layer that is exposed in the Red Rock Canyon area west of Las Vegas (refer to Trip 1 for a detailed description of this formation) and the Valley of Fire area to the east. It is an extensive unit of ancient sand dunes found throughout the southwestern United States that formed in an environment much like the modern Sahara Desert.

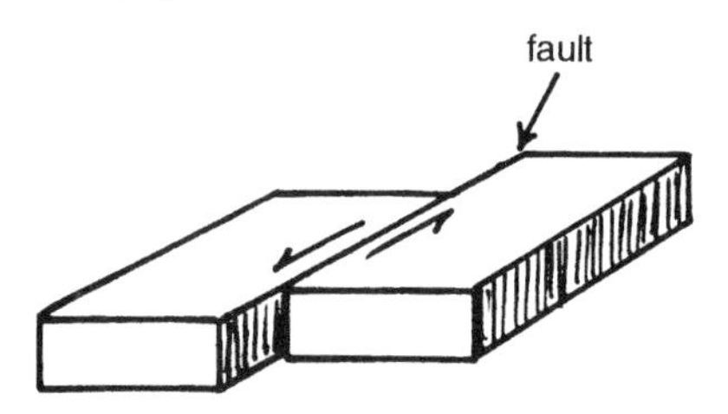

Left-lateral strike-slip fault. Each block appears to have been shifted left relative to the other.

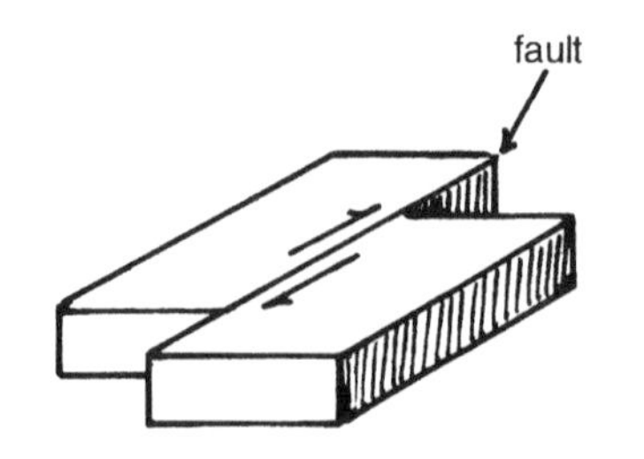

Right-lateral strike-slip fault. Each block appears to have been shifted right relative to the other.

AGE (Ma)[1]	FORMATION	MEMBERS	DESCRIPTION
	Muddy Creek Formation	—	Sandstone, siltstone, shale, and conglomerate
unconformity			
10.6 to 11.2	Red Sandstone Unit	—	Sandstone, siltstone and minor tuff (volcanic ash)
		Lovell Wash Member	Interbedded limestone, sandstone, siltstone, and tuff
13.4	Horse Spring Formation	Bitter Ridge Limestone Member	Mostly limestone with local sandstone, sandy limestone, gypsum, and colemanite
14.9		Thumb Member	Mostly sandstone with beds of conglomerate and gypsum
15.6 to 17.2		Rainbow Gardens Member	Limestone conglomerate at the base, overlain by limestone, conglomerate, dolomite, local sandstone, and magnesite in the Overton area

[1]Ma = Millions of years before present. Ages were determined using isotope or fission-track methods.

Miocene rocks in the Lake Mead region (after Bohannon, 1984).

5.0 The turnoff to Pabco plant and gypsum mine is on the left. Gypsum is a key component of many types of construction materials, notably wallboard (sheetrock), plaster of paris, and caulk. Other large deposits of gypsum that are now being mined in the Las Vegas area, such as the James Hardie Blue Diamond gypsum mine seen on Trip 1, are thick beds of nearly pure Permian gypsum that probably formed in a shallow marine environment. By contrast, the Pabco gypsum is mined from a deposit in the 8.5 to 5.0 million-year-old continental Muddy Creek Formation that consists of about 70% gypsum dispersed in clay and silt.

Gypsum is an evaporite mineral formed by evaporative deposition from seawater or from desert lake water in which dissolved salts become so concentrated that small crystals precipitate out of solution and settle to the bottom of the sea or lake. Another evaporite depositional process is evaporation of subsurface water that is drawn to the surface in arid areas by capillary action. The second process is thought to be a better explanation for the Pabco deposit because of the large amount of admixed sediments and the lack of definite evaporite layering. Other economically important minerals occur in rocks formed by similar evaporative processes including anhydrite, potash, borax, and salt. Deposits of the latter two minerals occur in Cenozoic rocks in the Lake Mead area. With the help of modern

Lava Butte.

chemical techniques, scientists can study the sequence of mineral salts in ancient lake beds and reasonably determine past climates, water temperatures, rates of evaporation, and the proportion of water that was evaporated to create deposits of various dimensions.

The low ridge on the right-hand side of the road is composed of conglomerates of the 20 to 8 million-year-old Horse Spring Formation. This sequence of sedimentary rocks was probably deposited in a large basin that was produced during the early stages of extension in southern Nevada. The Horse Spring Formation has been divided into four distinctive members—including conglomerate, limestone, dolomite, siltstone, sandstone, tuff breccia, and gypsum and magnesite layers—each deposited in a slightly different geological environment of periodic shallow freshwater lakes bounded by alluvial fans and pediments and lava flows from erupting volcanoes that blocked former drainage routes through the region. Tertiary sedimentary rocks in this area contain mineral deposits rich in manganese, lithium, clays, uranium, and zeolites.

The Horse Spring Formation lies unconformably on the Aztec Sandstone. More than 150 million years of the geologic record is missing between these two rock formations. Evidence from the Spring Mountains and the Red Rock Canyon area directly west of Las Vegas (refer to Trip 1) indicates that the early part of this time period was marked by mountain building and thrust faulting. The presence of mountains in this area at that time would favor erosion rather than deposition.

5.8 The prominent dark peak at 3:00 is Lava Butte. Lava Butte is composed of a volcanic rock called dacite, which has been dated at about 13 million years; so these rocks are very much younger than the Paleozoic sedimentary rocks of Frenchman Mountain. On a fresh, broken surface, the dacite of Lava Butte is quite attractive. It is light gray to lavender and contains visible crystals of mica, feldspar, and hornblende. The conspicuous dark coloration of the rock is rock varnish, a surficial coating of clay and manganese and iron oxides, the origin of which is described on page 94.

There is controversy among geologists about what Lava Butte actually is. Evidence shows that Lava Butte is either a small volcanic dome or plug that came up through the Horse Spring Formation and spread laterally for a short distance, or it is a remnant of a formerly more extensive lava flow that spread out over the surface during the time of deposition of the Horse Spring Formation. It is not a volcano. It stands up as a prominent peak above its surroundings because it is composed of rocks that are more resistant to erosion than the soft sedimentary rocks that surround it.

7.6 On the right and left sides of the road are several small dark hills. These hills contain blocks of Precambrian igneous and metamorphic rock that occur as large masses within the sedimentary rocks of the Horse Spring Formation. In places, the sedimentary rock layers that lie beneath these blocks have been disrupted and contorted. The blocks appear to represent large, ancient landslide deposits that were shed catastrophically into the developing Horse Spring basins about 16 to 15 million years ago. However, no rocks exposed in the immediate area could have been a source for these landslides. Some geologists believe that the nearest rocks that resemble these blocks are exposed east of Lake Mead in the south Virgin Mountains. This distance is too far for a landslide to travel. The source of these deposits is one of the many geologic problems that can be explained if the Frenchman Mountain block was originally situated 40 to 50 miles farther east and moved to its present position along faults.

7.8 Note the unnamed wash at right. This route crosses many washes (also called gullies or arroyos) which are tributary streams to the Colorado River. They are usually dry, but they were cut by water during cloudbursts and resulting flash floods, and some may have been permanent streams hundreds of years ago during wetter periods. They usually are cut through softer sediments and have distinctive gravel-covered flat bottoms and steep walls. The gravel moves along the bottom of a wash during floods, undercutting the softer sediments along the banks and causing them to collapse into the moving stream. Thus a wash maintains a flat bottom and grows wider while the banks remain steep and relatively parallel.

Unnamed wash during a flash flood in March 1992.

8.1 Enter the Lake Mead National Recreation Area.

8.3 The white rocks on both sides of the road are part of the 12 to 13 million-year-old Lovell Wash Member of the Horse Spring Formation. The white color of these rocks is due to the large amount of volcanic ash they contain. The source of the ash, which must have resulted from major explosive volcanic eruptions, has not been identified.

8.6 Hamblin Mountain is in the foreground at 10:00.

8.9 The road again parallels the large unnamed wash to the right.

9.3 Panoramic view. At 10:00, the Muddy Mountains; at 12:00, Black Mesa (flat top) with Hamblin Mountain in the background; at about 1:30, the northern Black Mountains with Fortification Hill, the dark mesa immediately in front of the higher peaks; and at 3:00, the River Mountains.

The Muddy Mountains (10:00), which contain Paleozoic rocks cut by Mesozoic thrust faults, are geologically similar to the Spring Mountains west of Las Vegas. This geologic similarity has led some geologists to propose that the two ranges were once part of a single geologic block before Cenozoic extension pulled them apart.

Black Mesa (12:00) is composed of basaltic andesite that was erupted from fissures and cinder cones between 10.6 and 8.5 million years ago. These lava flows are restricted to a relatively small area east of Frenchman Mountain and north of Lake Mead.

The Black Mountains (1:30) consist of Precambrian metamorphic and igneous rocks that were intruded by granites of the Wilson Ridge pluton 14 to 12 million years ago.

The River Mountains (3:00) are described in more detail in Trip 4. Briefly, this range is exclusively volcanic in origin. The range is the remnants of a major volcanic complex (stratovolcano and surrounding domes) that was active between 14 and 12 million years ago. (Refer to page 103 for diagrams of volcanoes.)

10.0 Crossing a major unnamed wash.

10.5 Lava Butte on the right at 3:00.

10.7 Intersection with Northshore Road (State Route 169). **Turn left (east) and proceed toward Overton.**

12.1 Cross Gypsum Wash. The road to the right (south) provides lake access. On the left (north) side of road is an unconformity between red tilted sandstone and siltstone of the Muddy Creek Formation (about 11 million years old) and tan flat-lying Quaternary sediments (1 to 2 million years old). This geologic contact provides evidence of the history of uplift, erosion, and deposition in the area in the last 10 million years. See color photo on page 23.

13.1 The Government Wash turnoff is on the right. **Proceed straight ahead (east) on Northshore Road.** At 2:30, the Black Mountains are in the background and Fortification Hill in the foreground. Fortification Hill is a remnant of a formerly more extensive series of Miocene lava flows (about 6 million years old), the youngest in the Lake Mead region. Researchers at the University of Nevada, Las Vegas, have identified several volcanic centers and more than 100 individual lava flows on Fortification Hill.

Hamblin Mountain.

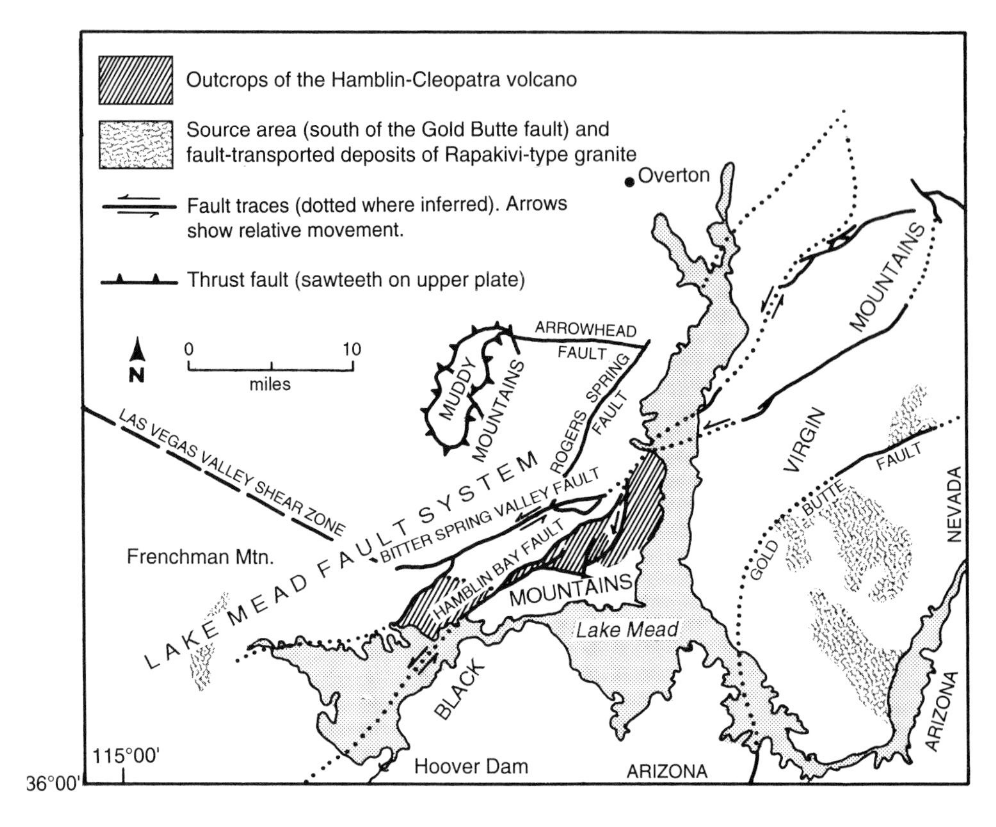

Major fault systems in the Lake Mead area.

14.8 The dark brown, rugged low hills in the middle distance at 9:00 are composed of late Paleozoic rocks (including the Kaibab Formation) surrounded by younger Cenozoic rocks of the Horse Spring and Muddy Creek Formations. These rocks mark the position of the Las Vegas Valley shear zone—the major, right-lateral fault zone that bounds Las Vegas Valley on the north.

15.0 Black Mesa lies directly ahead. The mesa is capped by a series of basaltic andesite lava flows known to geologists as the volcanic rocks of Callville Mesa. A few ancient volcanic vents have been identified on Callville Mesa located to the east.

Mesas such as this one form where rocks that are resistant to erosion (basalt in this case) overlie weaker rocks (siltstone in this case). The weak rocks on the flanks of the mesa erode readily, but the resistant caprock serves as a barrier that slows the erosional process.

16.4 The turnoff to Boxcar Cove and Crawdad Cove is on the right. Both roads are usually negotiable by ordinary passenger vehicle. Be careful though, because flash floods may have damaged the road since the last time it was repaired.

Black Mesa, looking east.

17.0 Roadcut between two low hills. These contain the ancient landslide and debris flow deposits of the Horse Spring Formation seen at mile 7.6.

17.2 The multicolored rocks on the right side (south) of the road are part of the younger members of the Horse Spring Formation. The white rocks contain significant amounts of volcanic ash; the yellow rocks are limestone deposited in an ancient lake; the black rocks are basalt flows that poured into the ancient lake.

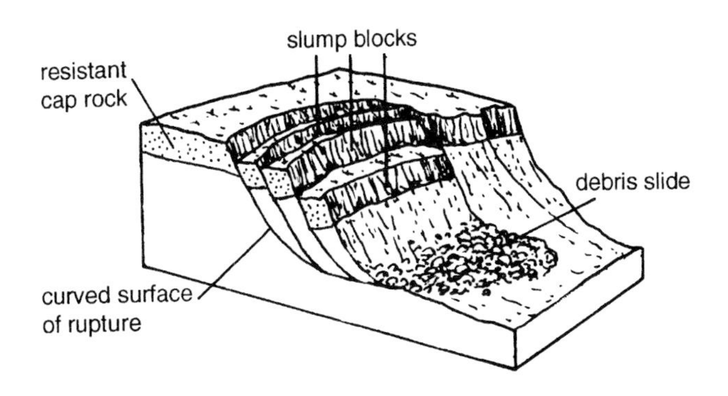

Slope failures and mass wasting in arid climates.

The sharp-crested ridges of the Bitter Ridge Limestone Member of the Horse Spring Formation.

18.6 The Callville Bay turnoff is on the right. This is a popular launch point for boaters on Lake Mead. Services include a small store, telephone, and campground. **Gasoline is not available.** Under the direction of the Mormon Church, Anson Call established Callville on the west bank of the Colorado River in 1864. For a short time it was a shipping point used by Mormon settlers. Steam-powered boats battled the rapids through Black Canyon, where Hoover Dam now stands, to bring supplies and people up river to the Virgin Valley area and northeast to Utah. This port was abandoned in 1869 when the transcontinental railroad was completed through Utah. The ruins now lie beneath several hundred feet of water.

19.6 Entering a geologically very complex area near the intersection of the two major strike-slip faults in the region, the right-lateral Las Vegas Valley shear zone and the left-lateral Lake Mead fault system. In this area of intersection of the major faults the rocks have been sliced, tilted, thrust over each other, and folded.

20.6 Cross West End Wash. The prominent sharp-crested ridges about 1 mile north (left) of the road are the tan to cream-colored limestones of the 13 million-year-old Bitter Ridge Limestone Member of the Horse Spring Formation. These limestones were formed as calcium carbonate precipitated in a freshwater lake that formed during regional extension in Miocene time.

20.9 Red Aztec Sandstone on both sides of the road. Note the black basaltic boulders littering the red outcrops (see color photo on page

23). The source of the boulders can be traced upward to a thin basalt flow capping the top of the surrounding sandstone hills.

21.0 Stop at the scenic turnout on the left side to see the multicolored Triassic rocks. Some of these rocks are stratigraphically equivalent to rocks that make up the Painted Desert and Petrified Forest of northeast Arizona. The vivid colors in these rocks are a result of a combination of normal weathering processes and a generally oxidizing environment. In this area, yellow colors are produced by hydrous iron oxides, red colors by anhydrous iron oxides, and black by manganese oxides. Combinations of these minerals produce the intermediate hues. Like cake coloring, a little goes a long way. A mere trace of an element can give strong color to a formation. In sandstones, the color is usually not in the sand grains themselves, but in the cement (silica, iron oxides, or calcium carbonate) between the grains.

22.3 The ridge in the background at 9:00 is composed of the gray Virgin Limestone Member of the Moenkopi Formation which contains some gypsum beds.

23.1 Lovell Wash. On the right (south) of road, notice the large blocks that have fallen into the wash because of undercutting by water during flash floods. Changes in bank configuration are rapid as a result of rare, but powerful, flash floods.

To the north, Lovell Wash hosts the Anniversary mine, one of several borate mines in the Muddy Mountains which produced borate from deposits of colemanite (hydrous calcium borate) in the upper part of the Horse Spring Formation. The deposit was discovered by F.M. Lovell and G.D. Hartman of St. Thomas. The mine, owned by West End Chemical Company, began production in 1921 and closed in 1928 due to competition from California mines. Total production was about 200,000 tons of borate. In this area, the Horse Spring Formation contains thin layers of algal mats (similar to stromatolites),

Large blocks in Lovell Wash.

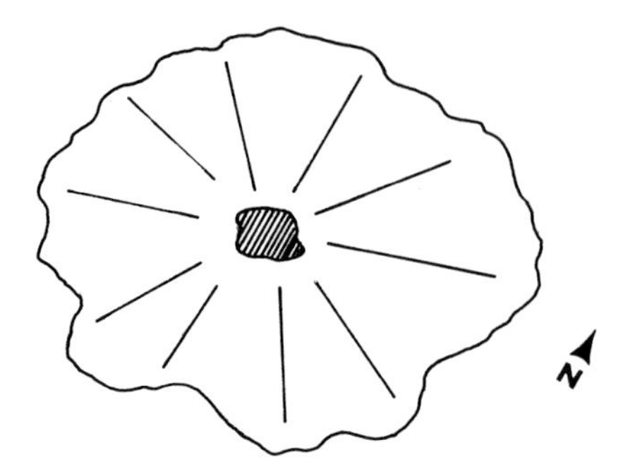

1. The Hamblin-Cleopatra volcano more than 13 million years ago.

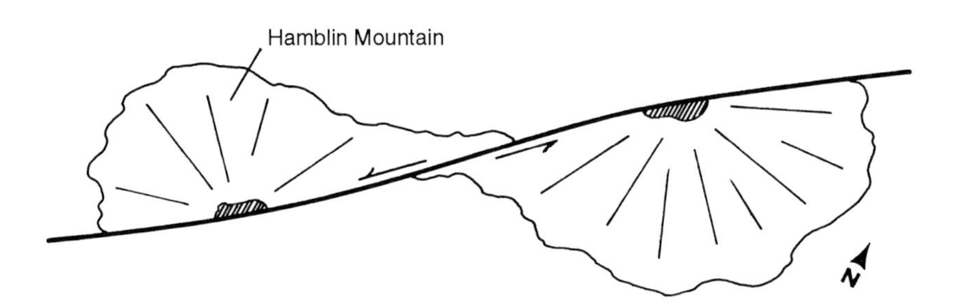

2. The Hamblin-Cleopatra volcano after about 13 million years ago.

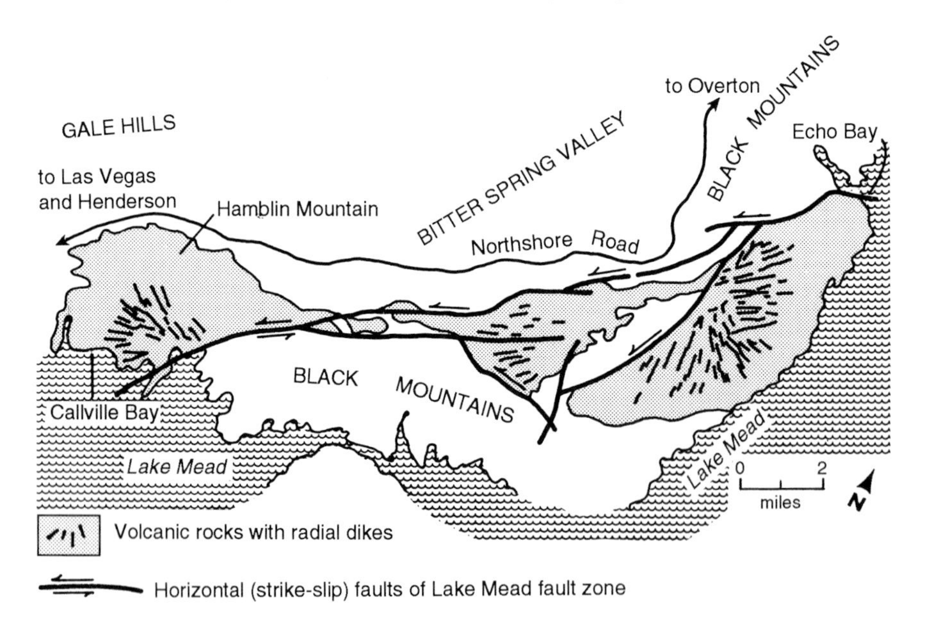

3. The Hamblin-Cleopatra volcano and the faults that dissect it as it appears today.

Reconstruction of the Hamblin-Cleopatra volcano (after Anderson, 1973; and Bezy, 1978).

Aerial view looking southeast over the tilted and faulted rocks of the Cleopatra stratovolcano. Hamblin Mountain stands alone in the right foreground.

fossil animal tracks, and ripple marks indicative of a mudflat environment. Borates have many uses, including making glass and cleansers.

23.4 Cross Callville Wash. The dirt road down Callville Wash (to right) is very rugged and should only be attempted in a four-wheel-drive vehicle.

23.6 The ridge of dark rocks straight ahead is part of the deeply eroded, 12 to 13 million-year-old Hamblin-Cleopatra stratovolcano. This volcano is cut by the left-slip Hamblin Bay fault which has displaced the northern half of the volcano, Hamblin Mountain, about 12 miles to the southwest from its southern half, the Cleopatra lobe. (The Cleopatra lobe may be explored ahead at mile 37.4.)

24.2 A syncline in the Bitter Ridge Limestone Member of the Horse Spring Formation is quite conspicuous on the left at 10:00.

25.1 Scenic turnout on the right. The Bowl of Fire is on the left (north). One can hike into the Bowl of Fire by walking across the alluvial fan, although no formal trails are present. Be sure that you have adequate footgear and plenty of water before undertaking this hike.

Talus cones southeast of Callville Wash.

25.7 Note the talus cones at 1:00. Talus refers to accumulation of angular rock fragments at the base of a slope due to weathering and periodic rockfalls. The weathered material is finer toward the top of these steep, very unstable slopes. As the rock debris grows upward, it protects the cliff from further erosion. Also look for slumps at the top of the mesa.

Syncline in Bitter Ridge Limestone member of the Horse Springs Formation.

26.4 **Turn off to view the Bowl of Fire.** The Bowl of Fire is an anticline—an up-arched fold that exposes older rocks at its core. The rocks in the core of the Bowl of Fire anticline are Aztec Sandstone. The younger rocks on the flanks include various members of the Horse Spring Formation that lie unconformably on the Aztec Sandstone. The geology of the Bowl of Fire is complicated by several faults.

Reservoirs of hydrocarbons can accumulate in geologic structures such as anticlines, provided there is a source for the hydrocarbons and the permeable and impermeable rock layers are in a favorable sequence. Shell Oil Company drilled the Bowl of Fire No. 1 well to 5,919 feet in the anticline in 1959 and found the rock sequence to be

Bowl of Fire.

similar to that in the Virgin Mountains to the east and in Frenchman Mountain to the west. Oil shows were recorded at 877 feet and at other horizons in Triassic, Permian, and Mississippian strata.

The dark rocks in foreground are the Rainbow Gardens Member (about 17 million years old) of the Horse Spring Formation. The high mountains at 9:00 are the Muddy Mountains.

Permian rocks crop out on the right (south) side of the road. Northshore Road follows the Lake Mead fault system—a series of faults with left-lateral displacement, measuring 40 to 50 miles (see page 74). Along this fault, rocks on the north side of road have been displaced west and southwest relative to rocks south of the fault. At this location, the fault places Permian rocks south of the road against younger Cenozoic rocks of the Horse Spring Formation north of the road.

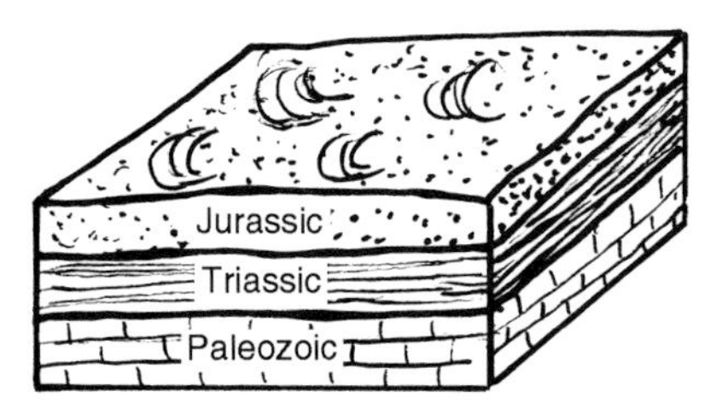

1. Deposition of Jurassic Aztec Sandstone in a vast desert (about 170 million years ago).

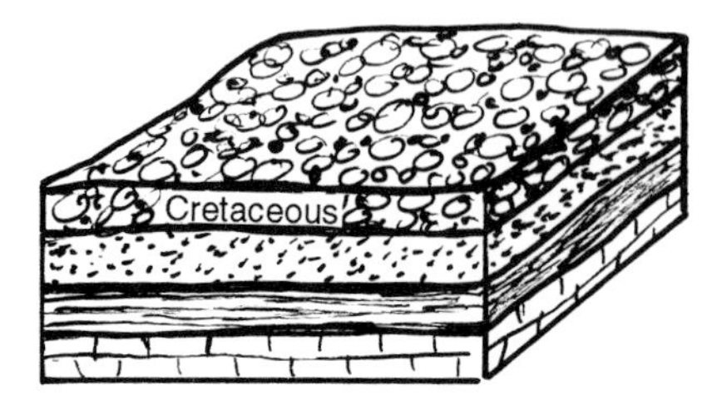

2. Deposition of Cretaceous rocks on top of the Aztec Sandstone.

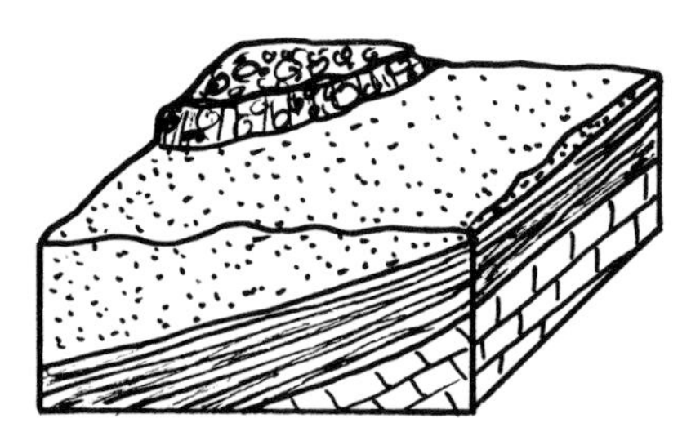

3. Uplift, tilting, and erosion of younger sedimentary rocks expose the Aztec Sandstone.

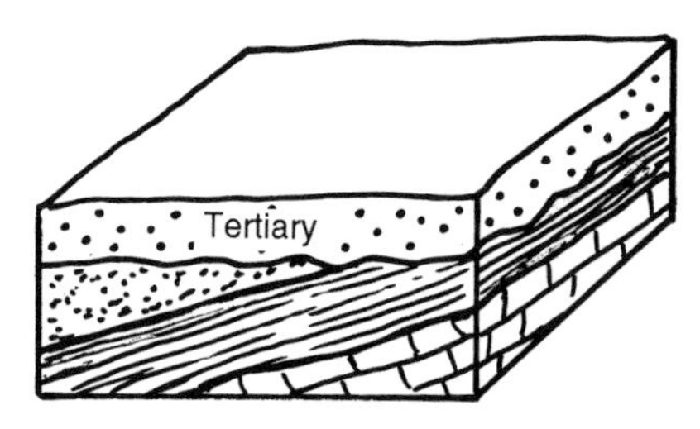

4. Deposition of river and lake sediments once again buries the Aztec Sandstone (about 18 million years ago).

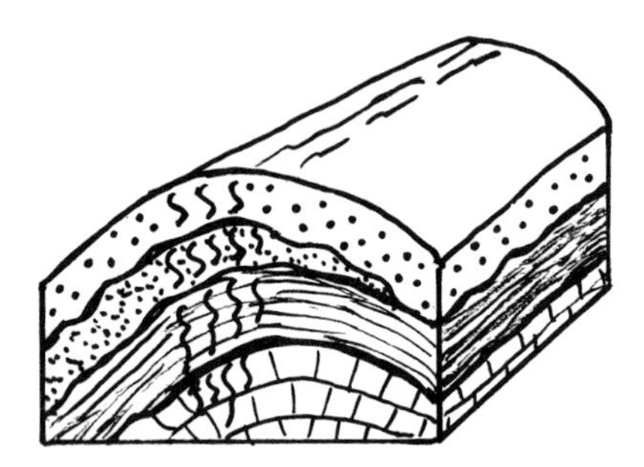

5. Folding of rocks forms an anticline. Folding causes rocks to fracture (about 11 million years ago).

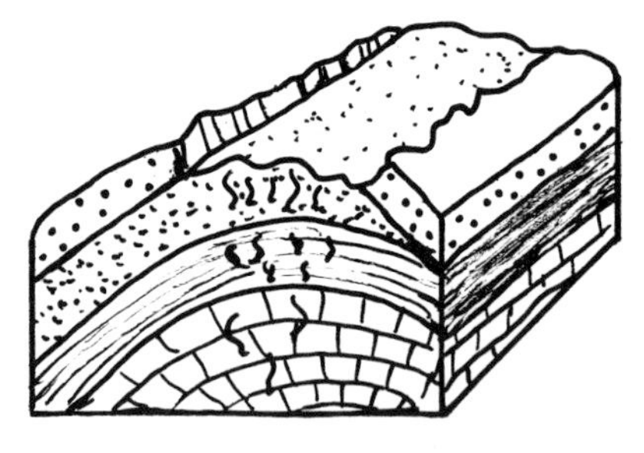

6. Weathering and erosion at the crest of the arch result in exposure of the underlying Aztec Sandstone (present time).

How the Bowl of Fire was formed.

27.3 At 10:00, rock layers roll over into a gentle anticline. Light-colored gypsum-bearing layers are exposed in the core of the fold.

28.1 **Turn off to small loop for access to Northshore Summit Trail on the left.** This short (1/4 mile) and easy hiking trail provides a panoramic view of the entire western Lake Mead area and part of the Las Vegas Valley.

Return to Northshore Road. Continue eastward and descend into Bitter Spring Valley.

28.6 The high peak in the distance at 11:00 is part of the north Virgin Mountains. These mountains, which lie east of Lake Mead near the Nevada-Arizona border, attain an elevation of over 8,000 feet. The mountains contain Precambrian igneous and metamorphic rocks that are overlain by Paleozoic sedimentary rocks.

29.7 Panoramic view of Bitter Spring Valley at 11:00. The prominent, discontinuous, pink-tan ridge in the distance is composed of the 13.5 million-year-old Bitter Ridge Limestone Member of the Horse Spring Formation. The fact that this relatively young rock unit is folded, tilted, and faulted indicates that a major period of geologic activity in this region occurred after 13.5 million years ago.

30.1 The dark, rough-textured rock in this area (look right at 2:00) is the Permian Kaibab Limestone. Its main constituent, calcium carbonate, was precipitated out of warm ocean water. This rock unit is exposed throughout the southwestern United States and contains over 80 genera of invertebrate fossils, along with sparse fossil fish teeth.

30.3 The route now passes through the Moenkopi Formation, composed mainly of reddish-brown, fine-grained siltstone and shale. Fresh surfaces display thin horizontal layering, ripple marks and mud cracks—evidence that this formation was deposited in shallow water.

These rocks were formed in a tidal flat environment that extended across the southwestern United States. Many tracks and trails of reptiles have been found in these rocks.

33.3 Aztec Sandstone. Pinto Ridge is ahead and to the right. The dark layer on the top of the ridge is the Rainbow Gardens Member of the Horse Spring Formation, which lies unconformably on the Aztec Sandstone. This is the same unconformity seen just east of Frenchman Mountain at mile 4.8.

33.8 On the right note the flat, step-like terraces midway up the ridge. They are remnants of ancient valley floors that were covered with sand, gravel, and cobbles from the ridge to the southeast, then were uplifted during Miocene time, and now are being dissected by streams to form a lower alluvial terrace. Geologists have identified two sets of successively lower (younger) terraces in this area which are evidence of at least two major periods of uplift. The highest flat-topped terrace is all that is left of the original valley surface.

Terraces near Pinto Ridge.

34.5 The Redstone picnic area is on the right in the red Aztec Sandstone. See color aerial photo on back cover.

34.6 The jumbled, rugged terrain north (left) of the road is known as the Echo Hills.

36.7 View to the northwest through Bitter Spring Valley. The dark-colored Muddy Mountains are visible in the distance at 9:00 (north). In autumn, particularly late September through October, it is quite common to see tarantulas crossing the road in this area. The high gypsum content of the rocks and soils in this area make it a harsh environment for many plant types, and water produced from springs and wells in these rocks is bitter to the taste.

37.4 The Boathouse Cove turnoff is on the right. For a walk through the ancient Cleopatra lobe of the Hamblin-Cleopatra volcano, turn right here and travel about 2 miles south to the intersection with Cleopatra Wash. A walk down the wash toward Cleopatra Cove will take you through the volcano's eroded interior where dikes of intruded magma form resistant ridges above softer, more easily weathered volcanic debris. (Refer to page 103 for types of volcanoes)

40.7 Cross Echo Wash. The ridges on the left at 10:00 to 12:00 are the East and West Longwell Ridges, named for pioneering geologist, Chester Longwell. Longwell produced some of the earliest geologic maps of southern Nevada and was among the first to recognize major geologic structures such as the Las Vegas Valley shear zone and the Keystone-Muddy Mountains thrust fault. His record of publication spanned six decades—from the 1920s to the 1970s—a remarkable career.

The Longwell Ridges are made up of Paleozoic limestone and dolostone similar to rocks present in the Spring Mountains west of Las Vegas. In geological terms, Paleozoic rocks in the Muddy Mountains, such as those in the Longwell Ridges, are more similar to those in the Spring Mountains many miles to the west than they are to the rocks immediately south of Northshore Road. Major strike-slip faults of the Lake Mead fault system form the boundary between these two different geologic blocks.

42.8 The turnoff to Echo Bay Road is on the right. Services available at Echo Bay include lodging, camping, gas, food, and boat rentals. The light-colored rock exposed for about the next mile on the right side of the road is called caliche, a naturally occurring calcium carbonate cemented rock that typically develops in arid climates.

Soils in arid climates are typically high in alkaline minerals because of the lack of rain and vegetation, both of which, in chemical interaction with the atmosphere and moisture, normally provide weak acids to soil. In addition, the limestone mountain ranges in the Las Vegas area provide abundant calcium which is leached out of the rock and deposited downstream on alluvial fans and other desert surfaces. Capillary rise of the water from below can also leach calcium from the eroded limestone pebbles that form the desert surface.

Caliche deposits along Echo Bay access road.

Moisture evaporates so quickly here that the dissolved calcium, combined with carbon and oxygen from the atmosphere, precipitates as crusts on pebbles on the surface and up to several inches or feet down in the subsoil. (In a wetter climate, the minerals would be washed away more effectively.) In time, the spaces between the individual pebbles in the subsoil will actually fill up with the calcium carbonate cement, forming a new sedimentary rock, caliche.

Caliche may vary in color from reddish brown (which means that iron oxide is present in the cement) to white. Silica may also be present with the calcium carbonate to form a particularly hard cement.

The Longwell Ridges terminate abruptly near here due to the presence of a major fault, the Rogers Spring fault. The trace of the

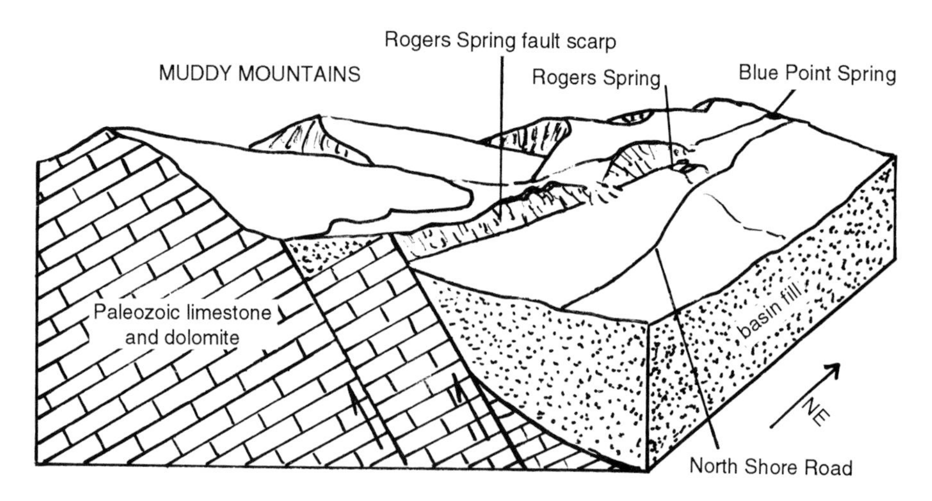

The Rogers Spring fault (after Bezy, 1978).

Rogers Spring fault is marked by a line of discontinuous springs along the cliffs to the left of the road. Springs occur here because movement along the fault has placed permeable rocks against impermeable rocks at depth. Groundwater that flows through permeable basin fill encounters the less permeable limestone and dolostone at the fault and migrates along the fault plane. The shallow groundwater, which reaches the surface in a few springs, is capable of supporting vegetation.

45.0 At 10:00, a cut bank in the wash exposes multicolored rocks. This exposure marks the trace of the Rogers Spring fault where resistant rocks of East Longwell Ridge are placed against easily eroded rocks of the Horse Spring Formation. A walk up the bank will reveal the evidence of faulting between the two rock units. Look for slickensides (parallel scratches on a polished surface that show the direction of fault movement) and breccia (angular rock fragments that were crushed in the fault zone).

The Overton Arm of Lake Mead is straight ahead. Overton Arm is the valley of Virgin River that was drowned as Lake Mead filled behind Hoover Dam. The Virgin River once joined the Colorado River just a few miles south of here.

Mountain man Jim Bridger passed through this area in 1826 and encountered helpful Paiute Indians who were living in the region at that time. In his journal he describes the "hilly barren appearance" and "terrible rocks" of the region. Explorer Major John Wesley Powell and his expedition party reached the confluence of the Colorado and Virgin Rivers on August 30, 1869 during their famous exploration of the Colorado River system.

The Virgin Mountains are east of the lake. The south Virgin Mountains are seen at 3:00. The prominent peak is Bonelli Peak. Some geologists believe that Frenchman Mountain originated near the south Virgin Mountains prior to its transport westward along the Lake Mead fault system and the Las Vegas Valley shear zone.

47.5 The turnoff to Rogers Spring picnic area is on the left (see color photo on page 24). **Turn in and park**. The spring flows year round at a high rate and a constant temperature of about 80°F and hosts many fish including perch, mollies, and golden shiners. Vegetation at this oasis includes salt cedar, saltbush, cattails, and palm trees.

47.7 Leave Rogers Spring area. **Turn left onto Northshore Road.**

48.3 A few small cottonwood trees are present in the wash to the right of the road. These are the first trees you have seen since leaving Las Vegas. The vegetation in this area consists mainly of blackbrush and creosote bush.

48.8 The Blue Point spring turnout is on the left. This is another small spring along the Rogers Spring fault.

49.3 The white, rough-textured deposit on either side of the road is gypsum of the Muddy Creek Formation (8 to 5 million years old). The gypsum was deposited in a playa—a lake bed that is usually dry but is subject to periodic flooding. The floodwater usually evaporates in a few days, leaving deposits of soluble salts such as gypsum and halite (common rock salt).

Magnesite deposits also occur in the Overton area in the Rainbow Garden Member of the Horse Spring Formation. Magnesite (magnesium carbonate) is almost pure white, very fine grained, and looks like clay. The major uses for magnesium compounds in the United States are magnesia refractories for use in metal, cement, and glass production furnaces; additives in animal feeds and fertilizers; and in the chemical processing of manufactured products such as rayon, fuel additives, rubber, pulp and paper, pharmaceuticals, and sugar.

There is a large salt deposit at least 1,750 feet thick (as shown by drilling in the lower part of the Muddy Creek Formation) in this part of the Virgin Valley area; however, surface exposures have been mostly covered by Lake Mead.

At the eastern end of the road to Salt Cove (just east of here) you can actually touch outcrops of salt that formed during the past 10 million years in playa lakes, and was then buried under hundreds of feet of younger sediments. Because salt is lighter (less dense) than the rocks burying it, it may have migrated upward as a plastic mass under the pressure of burial and tectonic forces that shaped the present topography.

Virgin Valley salt was mined by American Indians for hundreds of years before the area was settled by white men. This precious commodity probably was traded as far south as Mexico. Later, it was mined for use in mineral processing in Arizona and Nevada, but none has been mined in recent years.

50.1 Crossing Valley of Fire Wash. The large, dark green (in summer) treelike plants in the bottom of wash are mesquite (see color photo on page 24). Roots of the mesquite plants may penetrate to depths of 50 feet or more to reach subsurface water.

50.6 The turnoff to Fire Cove is on the right. The Virgin Mountains are in the distance across the Overton Arm of Lake Mead.

52.2 Mormon Mesa is straight ahead. The Muddy Mountains are at 11:00.

52.9 The turnoff to Overton Beach is on the right. Facilities and accommodations for fishermen can be found at the beach. Favorite fish are catfish, largemouth bass, and rainbow trout.

54.0 The turnoff to the Valley of Fire State Park is on the left. **Continue straight ahead for an optional side trip to the town of Overton (all services) and the Lost City Museum**. This side trip is about 16 miles round trip. **Reset odometer to 0.0**.

0.1 The road crosses a wash damaged by flash floods in 1991. For the next 2 miles, the route crosses through an area of wind-blown sand, eroded from the Aztec Sandstone bluffs to the west. This is a present-day example of how sand dunes form and migrate, grain by grain (refer to Trip 1 for more detailed information on dune formation).

1.6 Between 1:00 and 3:00 is Mormon Mesa. The mesa is capped by a resistant deposit of caliche.

2.5 The conglomerate layer on both sides of road ahead is tilted steeply to the east.

3.2 The flat mesa in the far distance at 3:00 (between the higher mountains) is the Grand Wash cliffs. The Grand Wash cliffs mark the topographic break between the Colorado Plateau and the Basin and Range physiographic provinces. The Basin and Range has been subject to major deformational events in the Mesozoic and Cenozoic Eras (discussed in the Introduction), whereas the Colorado Plateau has been deformed to a lesser degree.

Mormon Mesa, looking northeast.

3.6 Begin descent into Moapa Valley.

5.2 The flat-lying deposits along both sides of the road belong to the Muddy Creek Formation.

5.7 Pistachio orchard on right.

5.8 The road crosses another wash that flooded severely in 1991.

6.5 The Simplot Silica Products plant is on the left. Sand is mined about 4 miles southwest of here from the Cretaceous Baseline Sandstone. The sandstone contains nearly 97% silica. It is washed at the mine site and piped as a slurry to the plant, where it is screened. The final product contains more than 99% silica, making it highly desirable for use in production of glass and in the chemical industry.

6.6 Pueblo Grande de Nevada historical marker on the right.

7.7 Entering Overton. Many early explorers passed through this area in their travels to and from California. The names of Jedediah Smith, Kit Carson, John Frémont, and Jacob Hamblin are firmly established in the history of this area. The name Overton may be derived from the term "over town" which is how the inhabitants of the Mormon Hill settlement, established on the east side of the Virgin River, referred to the newer town over the river. The present site of Overton was selected in 1880, and transferred from Lincoln County into

Entrance to the Lost City Museum in Overton.

Clark County upon its creation in 1909. Many historic houses are still standing.

7.9 Entrance to the Lost City Museum on the left. This museum contains one of the most complete collections of artifacts ranging from the Desert Culture of 10,000 years ago, through the Basketmaker Culture which lasted until about 500 A.D., through the Pueblo culture from 500 to 1150 A.D., and followed finally by the Paiutes who entered the area around 1000 A.D. It preserves the story of Pueblo Grande de Nevada (the Lost City) which was situated near the base of Mormon Mesa on the east side of the Virgin River Valley (now the shores of Lake Mead). Scores of villages occupied the valley for a distance of almost 30 miles from before the time of Christ to about 1150 A.D. The latest inhabitants, the Puebloans, raised maize and cotton, mined salt and turquoise, and made fine pottery. Fay and John Perkins of St. Thomas "discovered" the sites in the early 1900s and excavations of the Lost City were begun in the 1920s.

8.6 Overton Food Town on the left. **End of optional trip to Overton. Turn around and proceed about 8 miles back to the Valley of Fire turnoff on State Route 169.**

Turn right into Valley of Fire State Park on State Route 169 and reset odometer to 0.0.

The geology of the Valley of Fire is very similar to that of the Wilson Cliffs-Red Rock Canyon area west of Las Vegas (Trip 1). In the Red Rock area, the dominant geological feature is the Wilson Cliffs-Keystone thrust fault system that places older Paleozoic rocks on top of younger Jurassic rocks. The same situation, with additional geologic complications, exists in the Valley of Fire. The main thrust fault in the area is the Muddy Mountain thrust. Because of these similarities, geologists have correlated these thrust faults and suggested that they are remnants of a formerly more extensive single thrust sheet that was dismembered by movement along the Las Vegas Valley shear zone.

1.4 Enter the Valley of Fire State Park. This is Nevada's first state park and was created in 1923 under the leadership of then-Governor Col. James G. Scrugham. Please drive carefully on the narrow roads and please do not collect rocks, fossils, or plants from the park.

2.0 Elephant Rock on the right (north).

2.3 Old Arrowhead Trail historical marker on the left. This is a remnant of a trail built in 1915 between Salt Lake City and Los Angeles. The cliffs on the right (north) side of road are composed of red Aztec Sandstone. The rocks in the low ground in front of the cliffs are part of the Chinle Formation.

The Chinle Formation consists of a thick sequence of shales which display a variety of brilliant colors ranging from blue, purple, pink, green, gray, maroon, to brown. Because shale is relatively soft and

Lost City Museum outdoor exhibit.

very fine grained, it weathers into slopes, gullies, low dome-shaped hills, and badlands.

Petrified logs.

2.6 John H. Clark historical marker on the left.

The hills in this area are covered with the silver gray desert holly. There is a striking variety of plant life that has adapted to this area. Hardy creosote bush, bursage, and brittlebush are known for their ability to survive in the hot desert. Another group commonly found farther north or at higher elevations because of its ability to adapt to cold conditions includes purple sage, blackbrush, and banana yucca. Still other species, such as Spanish bayonet and Mormon tea, have adapted to cold climates and the sandy soils produced by the weathering of the Aztec Sandstone.

3.1 Petrified logs on the right.

Several layers within the Chinle Formation contain petrified logs. The presence of petrified logs indicates that, at the time the Chinle was deposited in very quiet waters, extensive forests were present in this region. Some logs are several feet in diameter. This is the same rock layer that makes up the Petrified Forest in northeastern Arizona.

Petrified wood forms when fallen trees are buried rapidly by sediment. Rapid burial prevents decay of the trees. Groundwater that contains dissolved silica (usually derived from the weathering of volcanic ash) interacts with the cellulose of the wood and replaces it with very finely crystalline silica. Because the replacement process occurs on a molecular scale, the original patterns of the wood are faithfully preserved even though the composition of the tree or log has been completely changed from cellulose to silica.

Please do not disturb the petrified logs. Observe them in their natural state and leave them for future visitors to study and enjoy.

3.4 The Cabins picnic area to the right. These cabins were built in the 1930s by the Civilian Conservation Corps (CCC). They originally served as shelter for people travelling through the area.

4.6 Seven Sisters Picnic area. Brilliant red outcrops of Aztec Sandstone occur in the foreground on the left. The ridges behind these patches are composed of dark gray Paleozoic limestone. These rock units are separated by the Arrowhead fault, a major fault that runs essentially east-west down the axis (center) of the Arrowhead anticline, which forms the east-west-trending Valley of Fire. See page 22 for aerial view in color.

5.3 **Turn off to the Visitor Center**. This short detour is very informative and will enhance your visit to the Valley of Fire.

5.4 **Park at the Visitor Center**.

5.7 An **optional side trip to Mouse's Tank** takes you a few miles through a narrow canyon etched with magnificent petroglyphs and culminates in panoramic view. See page 25 for color photos of petroglyphs.

The Mouse's Tank road continues north for more vistas. When you're finished exploring this area, **return to the Visitor Center and turn right (west) on State Route 169. Reset odometer to 0.0 and continue through the park**.

0.4 In addition to the characteristic cross-bedding patterns (refer to page 38), two other features, rock varnish and differential erosion, typical of the Aztec Sandstone are visible at 3:00. The black, lustrous coating on many rock surfaces is called rock varnish. Although it forms in

The Cabins.

many environments on earth, from arctic to humid, it forms best in hot deserts and is often called desert varnish. Rock varnish is composed primarily of clay minerals (totalling 70 to 90% of the varnish) and oxides of manganese and iron and forms most commonly on hard, silica-rich rocks. The longer these rocks are exposed on a desert land surface, the darker they become. Several hypotheses of varnish formation have been circulated for many years, but it is generally agreed that the constituents of the varnish are derived primarily, if not entirely, from sources external to the rock they cover, for even the whitest sandstones—whether they be massive cliffs or small pebbles on the ground—can have this thin, dark mineral coating. The various hypotheses state that: (1) The darker iron and manganese minerals may be present in the sandstone and collect on the surface during weathering. (2) The minerals may wash over the edge of cliffs or percolate down through the sandstone from a dark rock or soil layer above and be concentrated on the sandstone walls. (3) Thin films of windblown clay may adhere to the sandstone walls absorbing any moisture present and drawing the manganese minerals to them through capillary action. The clay minerals may help deposit the dark manganese oxide that then cements the clay to the rock surface. (4) The varnish is formed by the concentrating and fixing of eolian (airborne) dust by slow-growing manganese-oxidizing bacteria in environments that receive intermittent flows of water over the host-rock surface. This latter microbial origin would also help to explain the widely varying rates of formation in different environments. Varnish forms in as little as 40 years in arctic or periglacial environments, but forms much more slowly in hot arid environments. Thicker and darker deposits with increasing age are conspicuous in the southwestern United States on late Pleistocene and Holocene alluvial surfaces.

In studying ancient rock art, researchers have found that some petroglyphs have become revarnished in time, and new petroglyphs have been scratched over older ones. From this, they have

Differential weathering in Aztec Sandstone.

determined that it takes about 2,000 years for the darker coatings to form in a hot, arid environment.

The second common feature of Aztec Sandstone outcrops is the occurrence of numerous holes in the rock that impart an appearance similar to Swiss cheese. Sandstone is nothing more than sand grains held together by mineral cement, usually calcite or silica. Some parts of the rocks are more tightly and completely cemented. These parts are more resistant to weathering and erosion than other parts. The incompletely or poorly cemented areas are more vulnerable to weathering and erosion processes and therefore wear away more readily creating the conspicuous holes in the sandstone. This process is called differential erosion.

1.9 Atlatl Rock is on the right; the campground and petrified wood walk are on the left. Atlatl Rock is another site of spectacular Indian petroglyphs. The side trip is about 1 mile round trip. When finished, proceed westward.

2.6 The Beehives. The Aztec Sandstone is faulted against Paleozoic limestone along the Arrowhead fault at about 10:00.

3.7 The road passes through Paleozoic rocks that lie above the major thrust faults of the area but the thrust faults are not visible from here.

4.0 Leaving the Valley of Fire State Park. **Proceed westward.**

4.5 The route passes through Permian red beds. (Refer to Trip 1 for information on the formation of red beds.) This entire sequence of rocks has been overturned (folded or tilted to angles greater than 90°). As a result, the older red beds lie on top of the younger Kaibab Limestone at this locality. Overturning of rock strata is common in regions of thrust faulting.

7.4 The well-stratified, variably colored limestones at 9:00 are part of the Pennsylvanian-Permian Bird Spring Formation. Many varieties of fossils can be found in this formation in the Las Vegas Range and the Arrow Canyon Range.

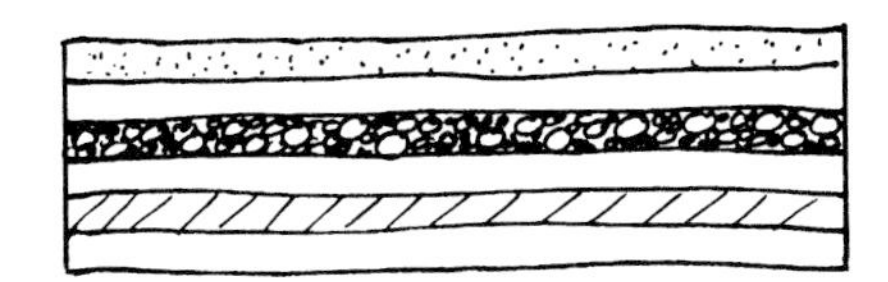

1. Undeformed sedimentary strata prior to thrust faulting.

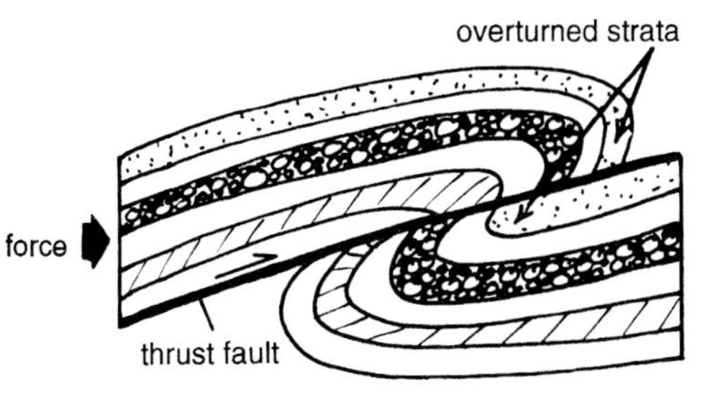

2. Folding and overturning of strata due to thrust faulting.

Footwall syncline (overturned strata resulting from thrust faulting).

9.1 Looking straight ahead at Arrow Canyon Range. This range is composed mainly of limestone and dolostone of Paleozoic age. The high range in the distance is the Las Vegas Range.

11.6 The Buffington Pockets area can be seen to the southeast at 8:00. In this area, the Aztec Sandstone emerges from beneath the Muddy Mountains thrust fault. As in the Red Rock Canyon-Wilson Cliffs area, this thrust fault places older Paleozoic limestone over younger Aztec Sandstone. The Buffington Pockets and nearby Colorock Quarry areas were the sites of petroleum drilling in 1983, although no petroleum was encountered. The Paleozoic rocks in Nevada are considered good targets for petroleum resources because of the abundant plant and animal material that was buried along with the sediments. In this area, they would be exposed closer to the surface—over younger rocks—because of their transport on thrust faults. This area is part of a larger belt of rock deformation that extends from Alaska to Mexico, and is known to geologists as the Overthrust Belt.

18.2 Intersection with I-15. Continue under the overpass to Las Vegas via I-15 South.

24.0 A playa occupies Dry Lake Valley at 2:00.

29.5 Pass exit for State Route 93 north to the Great Basin National Park. The park is a 5 to 6 hour drive from here.

31.2 The Chemstar Apex, Inc. lime plant is on the right. High grade lime is produced from pure Devonian limestone by roasting in large rotary kilns. Lime is used extensively in the production of masonry mortar and other building materials, as a flux in steel-making, as an acid-neutralizing substance in the processing of gold ore, in water treatment, and in glass manufacture, to name only a few uses.

34.9 Frenchman and Sunrise Mountains come into view at 11:00. The Muddy Mountains are at 9:00.

Las Vegas Valley lies directly ahead. The valley formed by extension during the Cenozoic Era. The Wilson Cliffs can be seen on the far side of valley.

38.4 Near this point the road crosses the buried trace of the Las Vegas Valley shear zone. The shear zone is a right-lateral strike-slip fault that has documented displacement of about 30 miles. The actual trace of the fault is not exposed because it has been inactive for the past 8 million years and is buried by alluvium of Las Vegas Valley. The presence of the fault is well documented by the fact that rocks north of the fault do not match those south of the fault.

Return to Las Vegas.

TRIP 4—LAKE MEAD, HOOVER DAM, AND NELSON

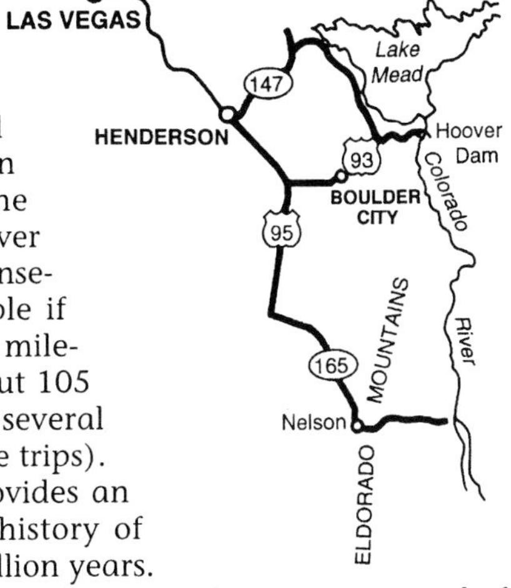

This trip begins and ends in Henderson and includes the River Mountains, Las Vegas Wash, the scenic west and south sides of Lake Mead, Hoover Dam, Boulder City, and an optional trip to the old mining town of Nelson and Eldorado Canyon on the shores of Lake Mohave. Roads near Hoover Dam can be congested on weekends; consequently, this trip will be more enjoyable if taken on a weekday. Total round-trip mileage, including the trip to Nelson, is about 105 miles (the odometer is set back to 0.0 several times in the log to allow for optional side trips).

The geology viewed on this trip provides an excellent introduction to the geologic history of the Lake Mead area over the past 15 million years. In middle Miocene time (15 to 12 million years ago), this area consisted of broad lava shields, stratovolcanoes, volcanic calderas, and broad intermontane basins. More recently, between about 12 and 9 million years ago, the upper part of the crust was pulled apart (extended) and cut by numerous faults. The rocks were broken, tilted, and moved, so that today most of the volcanoes are difficult for the casual observer to recognize. Beginning about 6 million years ago, cinder cones and basaltic lava flows formed at Fortification Hill, making these igneous rocks the youngest in the Lake Mead area.

0.0 Begin at the intersection of the Boulder Highway (U.S. 93/95) and Lake Mead Drive in Henderson. To get to Henderson from downtown Las Vegas, drive south on U.S. 93/95 or southeast on the Boulder Highway to Lake Mead Drive. **Set your odometer to 0.0 at the intersection and head northeast on Lake Mead Drive.**

Henderson came into being because of the country's needs during World War II and its proximity to a major source of electrical power—Hoover Dam. The United States needed a plant in this country to make incendiary bombs. Howard Eells, of Basin Refractories of Cleveland, Ohio, won the contract to develop the bombs at what became Henderson. McNeil Construction of Los Angeles built the plant which was first named Basic Magnesium. Production began in 1940, with magnesite mined in Gabbs, Nevada. After the war, the state of Nevada acquired the site and named it Henderson, after Albert Scott Henderson, a lawyer, district attorney, judge, assemblyman, state senator and Clark County pioneer who was instrumental in negotiating to have Basic's facility become the property of the state.

Five companies are now active in the Henderson industrial complex. BMI (Basic Management, Inc.) is responsible for the overall management and maintenance of the complex. TIMET (Titanium Metal Corp.) uses rutile from Australia and other sources to make titanium tetrachloride and titanium metal. The company also produces by-product magnesium chloride from magnesium metal. Kerr-McGee Chemical Corp. makes ammonium perchlorate, an oxidizer in rocket fuel, and manganese dioxide for dry-cell batteries. Chemstar Lime Company, Inc. calcines (oxidizes by roasting at high temperature) dolomite that is mined from a deposit at Sloan, south of Las Vegas. The resulting dolomitic lime is mostly used by the building trade in stucco and other products. The Pioneer Chlor-Alkali Company uses rock salt to produce chlorine, caustic soda, and hydrochloric acid. A large portion of Nevada's non-tourist industry is situated in Henderson.

0.5 There are excellent views of Las Vegas Valley and the Spring Mountains at 9:00. Frenchman Mountain and Lava Butte are at 10:00 and 11:00, respectively. The geology of these landforms is described in other road logs in this book.

1.7 Lake Mead Drive narrows to two lanes. The road is on pediment and alluvial fan deposits derived from the River Mountains to the east (refer to sketch on page 121).

2.0 Note the tilted Paleozoic sedimentary rocks of Frenchman Mountain at 10:00. (Refer to Trip 3 for a geologic tour through this area.)

2.2 Las Vegas Wash flows through the low area to the north (left), where vegetation is greener than elsewhere in the desert landscape.

2.7 The white rock at 11:00 is limestone of the Tertiary Horse Spring Formation. The limestone was precipitated in shallow freshwater lakes that formed when existing drainage systems were blocked by volcanoes erupting in the River Mountains and Black Mountain. The dark-colored rock above the limestone is a basaltic lava flow. Layers in the limestone are highly folded. These folds are probably not directly due to faulting, but resulted by the sliding of wet sediments into the basin. This process is known as soft sediment deformation.

3.2 Entrance to Calico Ridge Subdivision on the left.

3.6 The main water pipeline of the Las Vegas Valley Water Project passes beneath the road at this point. The water intake is located on Saddle Island in Lake Mead. Water is piped nearly 10 miles through the River Mountains to Las Vegas Valley. Approximately 70% to 80% of Las Vegas's water is delivered by this pipeline. The remaining 20% to 30% is pumped from deep wells in Las Vegas Valley. After the water is used, much of it is treated and returned to Lake Mead via Las Vegas Wash about 10 miles upstream from the Saddle Island intake area.

Water intake for Las Vegas' water supply at the southern tip of Saddle Island. Black Mesa is in the middle distance and the Muddy Mountains are on the horizon (looking northeast).

The rocks straight ahead are volcanic rocks of the River Mountains. Unlike most ranges that surround Las Vegas Valley, which are composed mainly of sedimentary rocks, the River Mountains contain mostly Tertiary volcanic rocks and Precambrian igneous and metamorphic rocks.

3.8 Las Vegas Parkway on the left is the main access road to Las Vegas Wash and the Lake Las Vegas project. Notice the large gravel operation about 0.3 mile north of the road. Gravel is being extracted from alluvial fans extending northward from the River Mountains.

4.1 The electrical transmission lines from Hoover Dam overhead. Only a small amount of the electricity generated at Hoover Dam goes to Las Vegas; most goes to Los Angeles, California.

To the left is the colorful panorama of Rainbow Gardens. Most of the rocks visible from the road are tilted steeply to the east and are composed of Tertiary sedimentary rocks deposited in broad basins 18 to 11 million years ago (Miocene time). The red pillars are capped by sedimentary breccia that is quite resistant to erosion. Large blocks of rapakivi granite and gneiss are common in this unit. The source of this obviously exotic material has long puzzled geologists. In the early 1970s Chester Longwell of Yale University and the U.S. Geological Survey proposed that this material was derived from the Gold Butte area 40 miles to the east.

Longwell postulated that the Las Vegas Valley shear zone, a right-lateral strike-slip fault, was responsible for this transport (see Trip 3 for more information on this fault and these rock units). A decade later, Ernie Anderson and Bob Bohannon of the U.S. Geological Survey also proposed the Gold Butte area as a likely source for this distinctive rock unit, but suggested that the deposits were separated from their source by at least 40 miles of transport on the left-lateral Lake Mead fault system (refer to page 68 for more information on strike-slip faults). The debate is still ongoing.

4.5 On the right are the tailings deposits related to milling operations at the Three Kids manganese mine.

5.3 Just ahead on the right is the entrance to the old Three Kids mine and mill. This is one of the major manganese mines in the River Mountains. These deposits occur in Tertiary structural basins adjacent to mountain uplifts. The manganese deposits at the Three Kids site were discovered in 1917 and actively mined until 1961. Small amounts of lead, copper, silver and gold were also recovered here. Manganese is needed to strengthen steel, and this deposit was very important during World War II. Currently, most of the manganese used in the United States is imported.

More than 2,225,000 tons of ore ranging from 15 to 40% manganese was mined and treated during the 44 years of operation of the mine. Manganese in the form of wad (hydrous manganese oxide) is the major ore mineral. Other reported manganese minerals are psilomelane, pyrolusite, manganite, and neotocite (a hydrous manganese iron silicate). In places the wad is partially opalized forming a hard glassy rock. The manganese at Three Kids may have been deposited by hot springs located along a major fault. Beds of manganese are associated with volcanic ash that erupted from volcanoes in the River Mountains. Minerals in the ash have been dated using the fission-track technique and suggest that volcanism and the formation of the manganese deposits took place between 12 and 14 million years ago. Other minerals mined from Tertiary basin sediments in the Lake Mead area include boron, gypsum and salt. Lithium, uranium, clays, and zeolites remain potential resources.

Access to the mine is strictly controlled. This and many other abandoned mines scattered throughout the Nevada hills can be extremely dangerous. The Nevada Division of Minerals has a good slogan: "Stay out and stay alive."

5.6 The route now crosses numerous lava (dacite) flows and sedimentary deposits related to volcanism in the River Mountains. The River Mountains, to the right (south) of the highway, are composed of tilted and faulted mid-Miocene (12 to 15 million years ago) lava flows composed of andesite and dacite. Two volcanoes, the source of most of the lava, have been identified in the River Mountains. The first volcano, located just north of Boulder City, is a stratovolcano

Open-pit mining at the Three Kids site. Note the folded Tertiary Muddy Creek sedimentary rocks forming a broad syncline.

High-angle normal fault forms the wall of a large open pit at the Three Kids site. At this locality, gypsum and manganese-rich sediments of the Muddy Creek Formation (left) are faulted against Tertiary volcanic rocks.

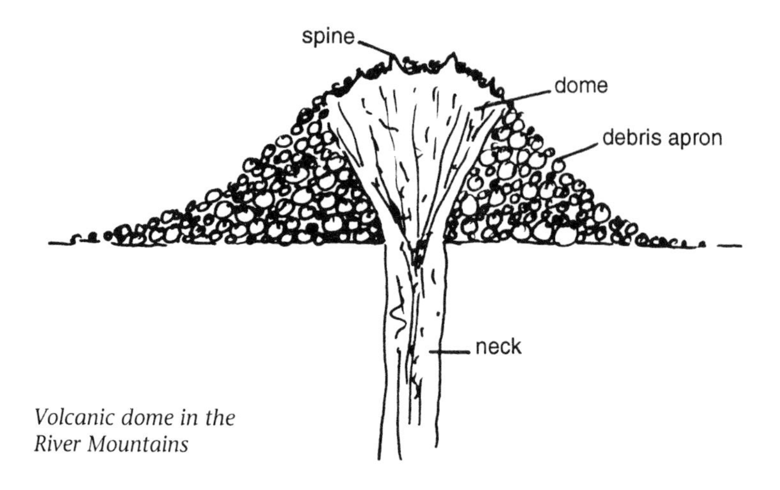

Volcanic dome in the River Mountains

surrounded by numerous domes. Stratovolcanoes are cone-shaped volcanoes, composed of andesitic and dacitic lavas interbedded with abundant agglomerate and breccia, that usually erupt explosively. The surrounding domes are formed by the eruption of very sticky lava such as dacite, which erupts to the surface but does not flow. It forms a low spine or a dome that quickly crumbles forming a ring of debris about the dome.

The second volcano, located in the northern part of the River Mountains, is a shield—a broad volcano composed of basaltic and andesitic lavas similar to those erupting on the island of Hawaii. The volcanoes have been tilted and broken into numerous parts producing a jigsaw pattern of rocks. Geologists try to fit the pieces of the puzzle together by studying and mapping these rocks in great detail.

Another type of volcano, not present in the River Mountains, is the caldera. Calderas are associated with violent eruptions of ash, rock fragments, and pumice which produce ash-flow tuffs (commonly rhyolite or dacite in composition). Because these volcanoes were later cut by numerous faults, they are now very difficult to recognize.

6.3 A good view of the Muddy Mountains at 1:00. The Muddy Mountains contain thrust faults that place older Paleozoic limestone on top of younger Mesozoic Aztec Sandstone. These faults are continuations of those in the Spring Mountains (refer to Trips 2 and 3 for detailed geology in the Muddy Mountains and Spring Mountains).

6.4 A good view of Lake Las Vegas and Las Vegas Wash at 10:00 (see color photo on page 26).

6.5 Entering Lake Mead National Recreation Area. Note the excellent view into Rainbow Gardens at 9:00. The Pabco Gypsum Company mine and mill are at 11:00. (This mill was used in the James Bond film "Diamonds are Forever.") Gypsum is being mined by open-pit methods from the Miocene Muddy Creek Formation. Gypsum is used primarily to make sheetrock or wallboard.

Sparse desert plants in this area include creosote bush, Russian thistle, skeleton weed, desert trumpet, desert holly, and brickellbush.

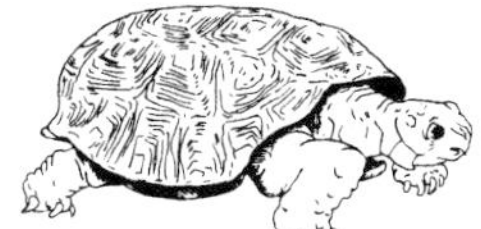

7.1 Junction of Lake Mead Drive with North Shore Road.

Turn left on North Shore Road (State Route 167) for a 16-mile round trip to Las Vegas Wash.

To the left at 9:00 is the Lake Las Vegas project. When completed, this project will contain a 350-acre, 2-mile-long lake, and eight major hotels, five golf courses, residential areas, and shopping centers. The lake is created by a 4,300-foot-long, 135-foot-high earthen dam and is being filled with water from Lake Mead. The dam creates a lake in the natural drainage of Las Vegas Wash, the only drainage outlet for Las Vegas Valley. Treated wastewater from Las Vegas passes beneath the lake through two 7-foot diameter pipes and empties into the wash downstream. These pipes or conduits are also designed to adequately handle flood waters passing through Las Vegas Wash. The outlets for these conduits can be seen at the base of the dam.

The prominent hill ahead is Lava Butte, which, as the name implies, is made of volcanic rocks (refer to Trip 3 for a detailed description). Lake Las Vegas is ahead on the left.

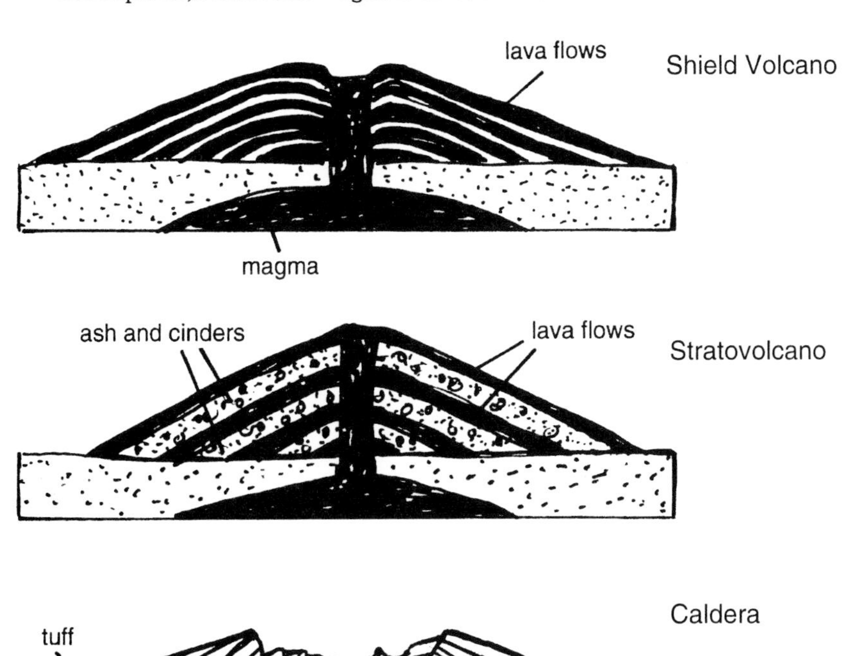

Las Vegas Wash, looking downstream from the bridge.

8.1 Cross the Northshore Road Bridge over Las Vegas Wash and park on the left (west) side of the road on the north side of the creek. The flat bottom is characteristic of washes, gullies, or arroyos in arid regions (refer to page 71, mile 7.8).

While attempting to navigate up the Colorado River, Lt. Joseph C. Ives reached Las Vegas Wash in 1858, believing it was the mouth of the Virgin River. Clear brackish-tasting water a few inches deep flowed out of it. He couldn't believe that the Virgin River, which he had believed it to be, could appear so "insignificant." Then and there he decided not to ascend the Colorado any further.

Lower Las Vegas Wash drains the entire Las Vegas Valley and has done so since early Pleistocene time. Looking upstream, the exposed sediments reveal a complex story of deposition and erosion extending back in time several million years. The oldest rocks exposed in the wash are red sandstone of late Miocene age (12 to 9 million years old).

The most conspicuous unit exposed in the wash is the coarse gravel named the conglomerate of Las Vegas Wash. It was deposited in a fast-moving stream with a steeper gradient than today as indicated by the size of the cobbles and the layering of the beds.

The cobbles are derived from the surrounding ranges and perhaps as far away as the Spring Mountains. They include all three major rock types: igneous rocks (granite, diorite, granodiorite, dacite, black fine-grained basalt and vesicular basalt with holes formed by escaping gas bubbles, and greenish-gray andesite), sedimentary rocks (limestone, dolostone, and sandstone), and metamorphic rocks (schist and gneiss).

Normally, this kind of young deposit can't be dated using current methods; however, researchers were able to determine the age of this formation by dating volcanic ash layers interbedded in the conglomerate. The distinctive chemical composition of the ash identified it as one that had erupted from Yellowstone Park 610,000 years ago. Thus, the conglomerate and the environment existing during its deposition could be dated. It is possible that at the time this conglomerate was being deposited high-energy streams flowed directly from the Spring Mountains into this wash. The eroded portion of the ledges of conglomerate seen in Kyle Canyon (refer to Trip 2) today may be the same conglomerate exposed here.

About 8,000 years ago, the southwestern United States experienced a great change in climate, and winter precipitation was drastically reduced. The wet climate of the late Pleistocene began changing to the arid climate that exists today. Along with this change in climate, perhaps between 4,000 and 1,000 years ago, Las Vegas Creek became an ephemeral stream, that is, it flowed only during storms when there was enough rain to fill the channel. This lasted until around 1955.

The bridge over Las Vegas Wash. Graffiti on the bridge demonstrates that there has been about 20 feet of downcutting erosion by the stream since 1983.

Dam for Lake Las Vegas on Las Vegas Wash upstream from the bridge.

Since 1969, the stream has been out of equilibrium. With every major flood, the stream deepens and lengthens its channel upstream toward Las Vegas. This is called headward erosion. The volume of sediment eroded from lower Las Vegas Wash from 1973 to 1988 exceeds the volume of concrete in Hoover Dam.

If left alone, the stream will eat its way into Las Vegas, adjusting its gradient so that flood waters will not move so fast as to erode more sediment than they deposit on their way into Lake Mead. However, in this process incredible destruction of manmade structures and natural habitats could occur. Millions of dollars have already been spent to repair bridges and culverts and to protect pipelines.

Current developments in Las Vegas have caused Las Vegas Wash to flow constantly from treated wastewater discharged upstream. This large amount of flow, about 900 gallons per second, along with the increase in floodwater which is discharged into the wash during storms due to increased paving in the valley, has caused considerable downcutting of the wash. At this locality, erosion has lowered the elevation of the stream by about 20 feet since 1983. The summer floods of 1984 were responsible for about half of this total erosion, dumping several million cubic yards of sediment into Lake Mead.

Treated wastewater (amounting to about three times the water taken from wells in the valley) flows down Las Vegas Wash into Lake Mead, which is the primary source of water for Las Vegas Valley. By federal agreement, Nevada receives an allocation of water from Lake Mead and is credited for water returned to the lake. That is, effluent that flows down Las Vegas Wash into Lake Mead allows Nevada to take more water from Lake Mead.

Return to the intersection of North Shore Road and Lake Mead Drive. Reset odometer to 0.0. Turn left onto Lake Mead Drive and continue eastward.

0.6 The route crosses sedimentary rocks of the Muddy Creek Formation. The unit erodes easily and it forms badlands topography and bluffs in the Las Vegas Wash-Lake Mead area.

1.0 Lake Mead is straight ahead. Black Mesa is at 11:00. Fortification Hill, at 2:00, is capped by lava flows of basalt that are about 6 million years old, and at 12:00, on the horizon, is Wilson Ridge in the northern Black Range in Arizona. Wilson Ridge is composed of a 13.4 million year old (Miocene age) quartz monzonite pluton. A pluton is a body of once molten rock or magma that crystallized below the Earth's surface. In this area many plutons represent the magma chambers that existed at shallow depths beneath the Earth's surface and supplied the molten lava for local volcanic eruptions.

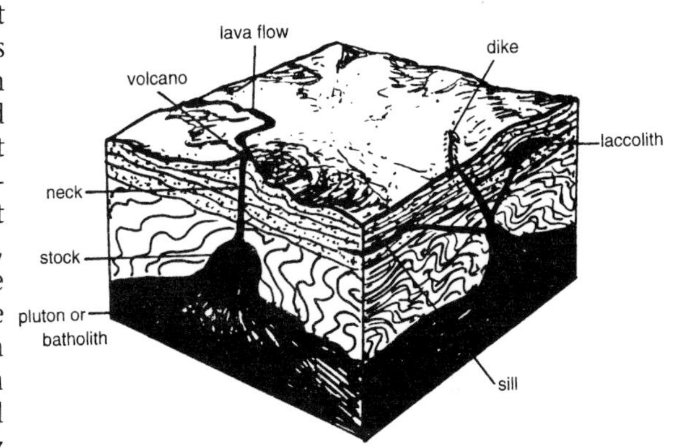

Cross-sectional diagram of plutonic and volcanic rocks.

Aerial view east over Lake Mead. Fortification Hill (middle) is capped by flows of basalt. Light-colored granitic rocks of Wilson Ridge are in the background.

1.8 **Lake Mead Drive becomes Lakeshore Road** at the intersection with the road (left) to the Las Vegas Wash ranger station, marina, and campground (see color photo on page 26).

2.0 For the next several miles the route crosses sheets of gravel shed from the eastern side of the River Mountains. These gravel sheets form a thin mantle over the volcanic bedrock and are called pediment gravels (refer to the sketch on page 121). In this area pediment gravels cover an older gravel and sand deposit known as the Muddy Creek Formation. Muddy Creek sediments were deposited between 9 and 6 million years ago during Miocene time.

Pediment gravels shed from the eastern side of the River Mountains.

2.5 To the right of the road (west) are exposures of volcanic rock of the River Mountains that protrude through the sheets of pediment gravel.

3.8 Junction of Lakeshore Road and the road to the Cliffs (on the left), and the main access road to the central River Mountains (on the right). The road to the Cliffs is a well-graded gravel road. Of geological interest at the Cliffs are exposures of the Muddy Creek Formation containing several volcanic ash layers. The age of these volcanic deposits is unknown, but the ash may have drifted to this area from large eruptions to the north in the vicinity of the Nevada Test Site. The road on the right is poor and is only recommended for high-clearance, four-wheel-drive vehicles. Continue on Lakeshore Road.

4.1 At 3:00 on the skyline are the faulted remains of the volcano from which much of the basalt in the northern part of the River Mountains was erupted. About 12 million years ago it may have resembled the broad shield volcanoes on the island of Hawaii.

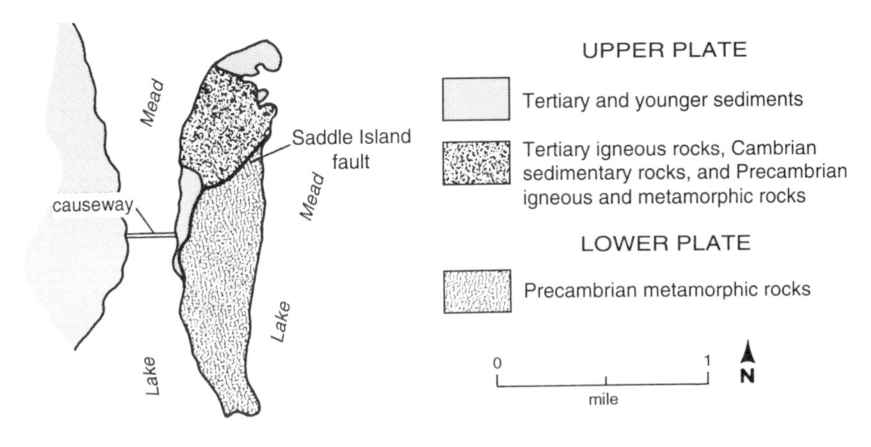

4.8 The igneous rocks dacite and basalt are exposed along the road at 9:00. This area contains five small volcanoes or volcanic domes of Miocene age.

5.7 Junction with road to the Lake Mead Fish Hatchery.

5.8 At 10:00 there is a good view of the northern part of Saddle Island. This part of the island forms the upper plate of the Saddle Island detachment fault. (Refer to the sketch on page 125 for more information on detachment faults.) Notice the prominent saddle on the north side of the island. The detachment fault is exposed on the north side of the saddle and divides the island into two plates. Note the color change associated with the fault. The upper plate rocks are light red and the lower plate rocks are green (see color photo on page 27).

Aerial view of Saddle Island.

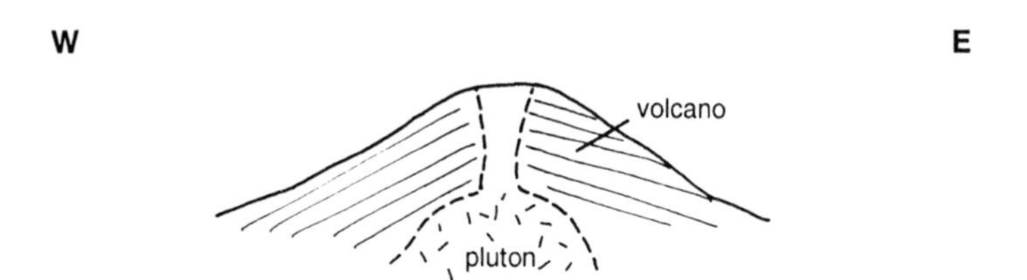

1. River Mountains volcano before 13.4 million years ago.

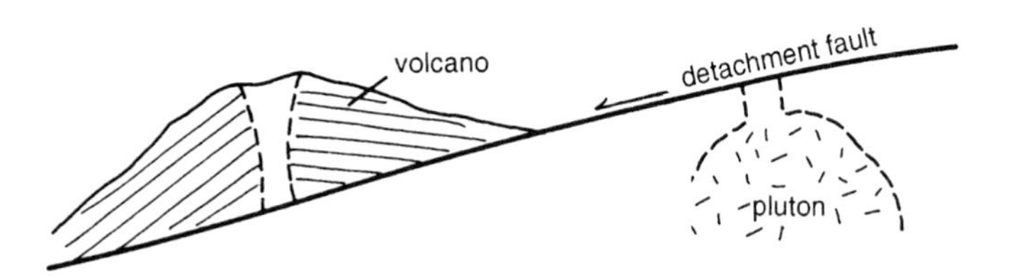

2. River Mountains volcano after 13.4 million years ago. Detachment fault has dissected it.

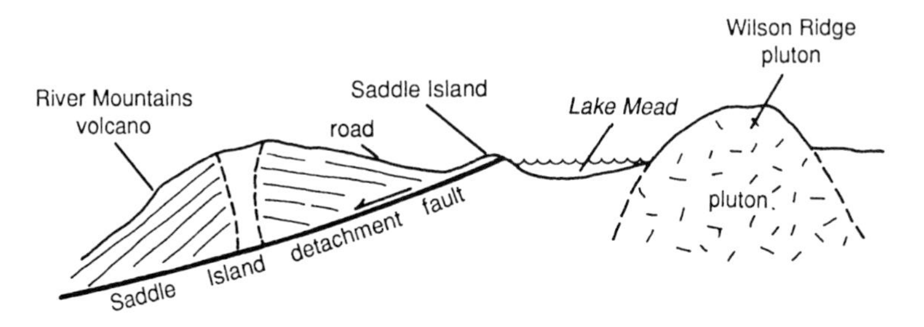

3. River Mountains volcano as it appears today after erosion. Plane of thrust fault is preserved only under the River Mountains.

River Mountains and Wilson Ridge pluton separated by the Saddle Island detachment fault.

In 1987 geologists Mike Weber and Eugene Smith, of the University of Nevada, Las Vegas, suggested that the Saddle Island fault was the most important fault in this part of the Lake Mead area. They proposed that the volcanoes of the River Mountains were once positioned over the granites of the Wilson Ridge (the prominent ridge across the lake). The Wilson Ridge granites may represent the magma chamber that fed volcanic rocks in the River Mountains. They believe that about 13.4 million years ago, a detachment fault (the Saddle Island fault) formed between the River Mountains and the Wilson Ridge pluton and carried the River Mountains about 12 miles westward to their present location.

Access to Saddle Island is limited and there is a locked gate on the west side of the causeway leading to Saddle Island. Permission to walk the causeway to the detachment fault may be obtained from the offices of the Southern Nevada Water Project.

6.1 Straight ahead is a panorama of the northern part of the Eldorado Range. This part of the range is composed of the Boulder City pluton, a middle Miocene quartz monzonite intrusion. At 1:00 is the rugged core of the River Mountains stratovolcano (refer to page 103).

6.5 The road now leaves the rolling terrane characteristic of the Muddy Creek Formation and enters the relatively flat alluvial deposits derived from the River Mountains.

6.6 Entrance to the Southern Nevada Water System and Saddle Cove to the left.

7.3 Boulder Bay turnoff to the left. The black Fortification Hill is at 9:00 with the light-colored Wilson Ridge pluton behind it and to the right.

7.6 Note the quarry in dacite at 3:00. This volcanic unit is named the dacite of Teddy Bear Wash for a stand of Teddy Bear cholla (cactus) in the eastern River Mountains. The quarried rock was used to construct the causeway to Saddle Island, and was recently used as fill to reconstruct the southern breakwater at Lake Mead Marina.

8.0 Entering the congested area near Boulder Beach and Lake Mead Marina. The road to the right goes to National Park Service employee dwellings.

8.1 Lake Mead Marina to the left.

8.7 Junction with road to Lake Mead Lodge on the left. To the left are two isolated buttes of dacite and dacite breccia. Volcanoes are relatively short-lived phenomena. They erode rather rapidly and commonly are surrounded by aprons of debris eroded from their flanks. The massive cliffs behind the two buttes represent the debris apron that at one time existed around the River Mountains stratovolcano.

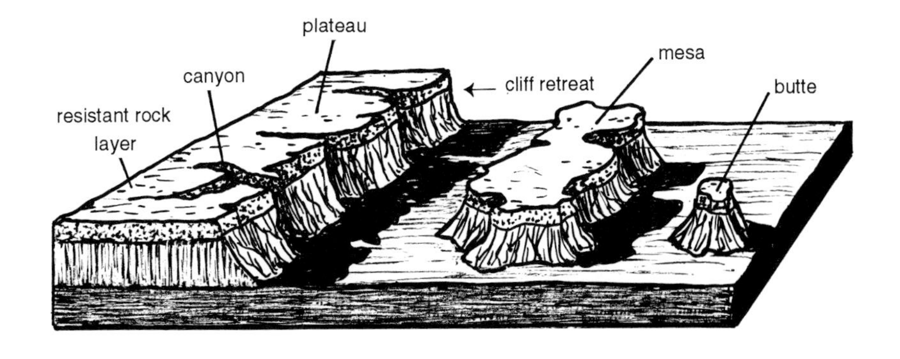

9.0 The road on the left is an entrance to Boulder Beach and the Lake Mead Campground. The small general store at the campground is an excellent place to stop for lunch, soft drinks, etc.

Eroded central crater area of the River Mountains stratovolcano.

9.2 To the left is another road to the Boulder Beach campground.

9.6 In the foreground at 3:00 is the eroded central crater area of the River Mountains stratovolcano. Light-colored rocks form the River Mountains quartz monzonite pluton which occupies the vent area of the volcano. Reddish rocks above the intrusion are altered andesite and plutonic rock cut by numerous dacite dikes that emanate outward from the River Mountains pluton. The alteration was caused by heat from the intruding pluton and by circulating warm water. The alteration products are primarily iron oxide and clay accompanied by the minerals barite, specular hematite, and manganese oxides. The dark rocks at the summit are andesite and dacite flows that formed on the flanks of the stratovolcano. This view of the River Mountains provides a excellent geologic section through the core of a volcano.

At this point the road crosses the trace of the Hamblin Bay fault, one of the strike-slip faults that collectively form the Lake Mead fault zone. It is postulated that the southern terminus of this fault zone may end in Hoover Dam or extend southeastward through Eldorado Valley. (Refer to map on page 74)

The route now traverses modern gravel deposits of Hemenway Wash. At 2:00 note the water storage tank and beautiful homes in Boulder City.

Straight ahead is a good view of the Boulder City pluton. The pluton varies in composition from diorite to quartz monzonite and appears to have two topographic expressions. The uppermost exposures are composed of smooth rolling hills; the lower part is composed of rugged cliffs. Various interpretations have been postulated; however, Ernie Anderson of the U.S. Geological Survey suggested that the difference in appearance of the rock is due to the presence of a paleohydrologic surface (or ancient water table). Rocks below the surface have been highly altered by circulating warm water and the rocks above are relatively fresh. This surface forms a "bathtub ring" on both sides of Hemenway Wash.

10.2 The road on left is the access route to Hemenway Marina.

10.6 At 9:00 are exposures of highly altered dacite flows overlain by (or in fault contact with) dark-gray to black flows of dacite.

11.1 Junction of Lakeshore Drive with U.S. 95. The Alan Bible Visitors Center for the Lake Mead National Recreation Area is on the right. Take time to browse through the interesting displays about the human and natural history of the Lake Mead area. There is also a desert garden and a well marked nature trail. The bookstore at the visitors' center has a good selection of books and maps that describe the recreation area.

Turn left on U.S. 93 and proceed toward Boulder Dam.

11.2 Excellent view of Lake Mead and Saddle Island at 9:00.

11.6 Gold Strike Inn Casino and Hotel is on the left and a gas station is on the right.

For the next mile, the road follows a strike-slip fault that lies within the Lake Mead fault zone. Intrusive rocks of the Boulder City

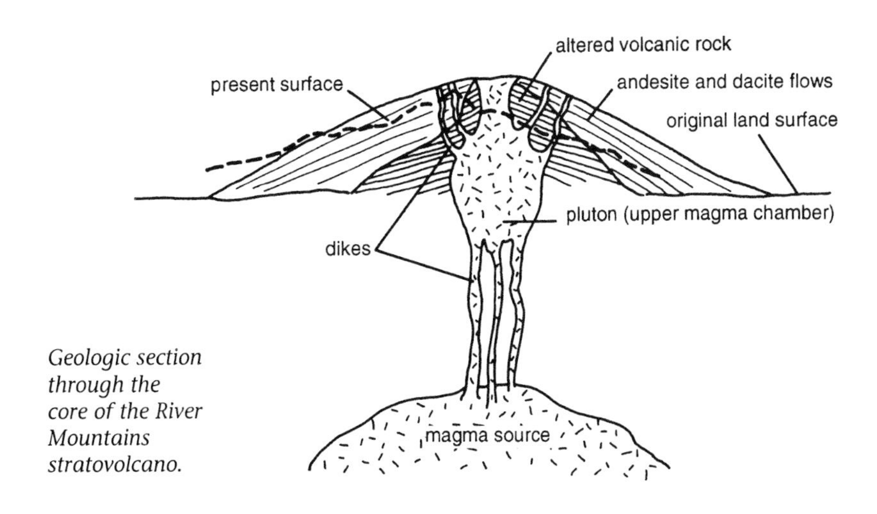

Geologic section through the core of the River Mountains stratovolcano.

pluton are faulted against Miocene age volcanic flows and sedimentary units. Note the numerous fault surfaces (slickensides) and evidence of hematite alteration in exposures on the north (left) side of the highway.

Looking east toward the Gold Strike Inn Casino. Dark Miocene volcanic rocks are in the foreground. Light-colored granitic rocks of the Wilson Ridge pluton are on the horizon with part of Fortification Hill just to the left.

12.0 The road begins to descend to Hoover Dam. The deep canyon on the right is Gold Strike Canyon. This canyon provides a popular route to hot springs just below Hoover Dam.

12.1 The road to the right provides access to the Boulder City pluton and Gold Strike Canyon.

12.4 Excellent view of Gold Strike Canyon on the right and altered volcanic rocks along the strike-slip fault in the roadcut on the left. Gold Strike Canyon is cut almost entirely into intrusive rocks of the Boulder City pluton.

13.0 S-curves on U.S. 93 and excellent views into Gold Strike Canyon. Note the polished and striated fault surfaces (slickensides) in exposures on left side of road. Be careful, many accidents have occurred here!

13.4 Turn off to Lakeview Point on the left. This stop provides an excellent panorama of Lake Mead.

Past the road to Lakeview Point, the nature of the rocks changes completely. The first exposures of a geologic unit called the tuff of Hoover Dam are encountered. This volcanic unit erupted explosively about 14.3 million years ago (during Miocene time) and may have formed a caldera just northwest of Hoover Dam.

13.5 Lower Portal Road to the right. This road is a direct route to the base of Hoover Dam, but access is strictly controlled by the U.S. Bureau of Reclamation.

On the left side of the road is the main warehouse for Hoover Dam. This is a good area to view mountain sheep at sunset.

13.6 Information sign and parking area for Hoover Dam on the right. For the next mile the road cuts through exposures of the tuff of Hoover Dam.

14.4 The road begins its steep descent to Hoover Dam. Note the excellent exposures of fault surfaces on the right side of road. Sugarloaf Peak is at 12:00 across the Colorado River in Arizona. It is composed of dacite flows at the top and the tuff of Hoover Dam below.

14.6 A basalt dike cuts the tuff of Hoover Dam in exposures on the left side of highway.

14.9 Begin crossing Hoover Dam.

15.0 Entering Arizona.

15.1 Just ahead, notice the beautifully exposed polished and striated fault surface. The road sign directional arrow must have been positioned by a geologist. The arrow corresponds to the direction of motion of the fault (right-lateral).

15.4 Turn left into the parking lot. Park your vehicle and walk back to the dam.

Aerial view of Hoover Dam.

Boulder Dam construction in the mid-1930s. Photo courtesy of the Nevada Historical Society.

U.S. Post Office in St. Thomas being covered by the rising waters of the Overton Arm of Lake Mead, 1938. Photo courtesy of the Nevada Historical Society.

Hoover Dam is named after Herbert Hoover, 31st President of the United States. Construction on Hoover Dam began in 1931–during the Depression–and was completed in 1935, two years ahead of schedule and under budget! The many stories of leadership and engineering technology–from the planning through building stages of the dam–are well worth reading more about. The dam is 726 feet high, 1,244 feet long at its crest, and 660 feet thick at its base. The dam was built for flood control on the Colorado River and hydroelectric energy production, and produced Lake Mead, America's largest manmade reservoir. It was named for Dr. Elwood Mead, Reclamation Commissioner during the dam's construction. The depressing side to this engineering wonder is that magnificent canyons full of beauty and archaeological and historical riches were sacrificed forever for the enjoyment and wonder of future generations. Of the electricity produced here, only 8.8% is allotted to southern Nevada. Tours of Hoover Dam are conducted daily. Tickets may be purchased here. There is also an exhibit building on the Nevada side. Take time to visit the various visitor's exhibits. The route then returns to Henderson via Boulder City.

Reset odometer to 0.0 at the winged statue on the north side of the dam and continue on to Boulder City.

1.5 The lower Portal Road is to the left.

1.6 The Lakeview Point turnoff is on right.

1.9 S-curves on U.S. 93 and excellent views into Gold Strike Canyon on left.

3.2 The Gold Strike Inn Casino and Hotel is on the right and a gas station is on the left.

3.7 A good view of Lake Mead and Saddle Island at 3:00.

3.9 Junction of Lakeshore Drive with U.S. 95. The Alan Bible Visitors Center for the Lake Mead National Recreation Area is on the right. Continue straight ahead on U.S. 95.

4.3 At 2:00 there are good views of the eroded central crater area of the River Mountains stratovolcano. See page 27 for color photo.

5.6 Entering Boulder City which was originally built to serve as a supply center for construction of Hoover Dam and to house the workers who flooded here to find work during the Depression. Some workers were lucky enough to live in the dormitories provided by the Six Companies, Inc.

At the end of 1935, as the dam neared completion, the workers began to leave, looking for new work. Buildings were dismantled or moved to other parts of the state; the trees and grass died. In some areas only paved streets and sidewalks remained. But the Bureau of Reclamation kept their offices there to oversee the operation of the

Panoramic view of Boulder City looking south in October 1933.
Photo courtesy of the Nevada Historical Society.

dam and the U.S. Bureau of Mines opened a branch office for a few years to sample ores in the region. A few original residents stayed on, using discarded materials from other abandoned buildings to build their homes and churches. Boulder City remained a federal reservation (no gambling, no liquor) until 1960, when it became a regular chartered Nevada town. Facilities still remain limited, and gambling is still not allowed, but it is a charming town with a quiet and stable atmosphere. Property is much sought after by retirees wishing to live in a small-town environment.

Looking southeast at Boulder City in 1993 from the summit of Red Mountain in the River Mountains north of town.

6.5 Intersection of business route to Boulder City on the left and U.S. 93 bypass straight ahead. Historic Boulder City is on the left. **Continue straight ahead**.

7.3 The turnoff to the River Mountains hiking trail is on the right. There is no sign for the hiking trail on the north side of U.S. 93, but there is a sign on the south side along with a small parking area and display area. The hiking trail follows trails blazed by the Civilian Conservation Corps (CCC) in the 1930s and continues for nearly 3 miles to the summit of Black Mountain. There are excellent views of Lake Mead from the summit. The trail ascends through "Red-Black" canyon to the saddle just below the Boulder City VORTAC, an

Hikers near the summit of Black Mountain on the River Mountain trail.

aircraft navigation facility at the summit of Red Mountain. A major fault in the canyon places Miocene volcanic rocks of the River Mountain stratovolcano (black colored) against highly altered older Miocene volcanic rocks. Paleozoic limestone and dolomite of the Mississippian Callville Formation locally crop out on the east side of "Red-Black" canyon and are the remnants of a mountain range that once existed in this area. The range was buried by volcanic rock and intruded by rising magma during the formation of the River Mountains stratovolcano. Follow the trail to the east through the saddle and climb through flows on the flanks of the River Mountains stratovolcano. The hike is recommended only for individuals in good health. Sturdy hiking shoes or boots are recommended. Bring plenty of water if you attempt the hike in late spring or early fall. The hike is not recommended during the summer because mid-day temperatures may reach 110 °F.

8.0 Intersection of the U.S. 93 bypass with the Boulder City business route. **Turn right at the traffic light onto U.S. 93 to Las Vegas.**

8.6 On the right, Yucca Drive provides access to the southern part of the River Mountains and hiking trails. Follow this road to the entrance to the microwave station. Benches have been installed for visitors to enjoy the beautiful views of Las Vegas and Boulder City from the top.

9.0 The rocks to the right (north) of U.S. 93 are volcanic rocks that were intruded by the Boulder City pluton. They consist of basalt, andesite, and dacite flows that dip gently to the east.

The jagged peaks of the Railroad Pass pluton are straight ahead. The pluton is probably part of the Boulder City pluton and is composed of granite and quartz monzonite.

10.4 Junction of U.S. 95 south to Searchlight. **Turn left (south) on U.S. 95 to Searchlight** for the optional side trip to Nelson and Eldorado Canyon. **Set odometer to 0.0.**

0.0 This 58-mile round trip to Nelson begins by crossing broad valleys that are characteristic of the Basin and Range geomorphic province—a region characterized by north-trending mountain ranges separated by broad valleys. This province extends from southern Idaho through Nevada and Utah into Arizona, New Mexico, westernmost Texas, and well into Mexico. In the Basin and Range, major faults generally form the borders of the mountain ranges. The Basin and Range province as we see it today began forming about 30 million years ago when a period of major thinning or extension of the Earth's crust began. In some places the crust has been extended by as much as 300%. Crustal thinning was accompanied by the eruption of numerous volcanoes. On this side trip many examples of the crustal extension and volcanism that created the Basin and Range province may be observed.

The volcanoes are Miocene shields and low stratovolcanoes composed of andesitic and dacitic lavas interbedded with abundant agglomerate and breccia (sketches of types of volcanoes are on page 103).

0.5 Ahead, the north-trending Eldorado Valley is typical of basins in the Basin and Range province in that it has no drainage outlet. All drainage is toward a lake bed, or playa, in the center of the basin. Alluvial fans spread from the mountain ranges toward the playa. Eroded bedrock mantled by alluvium close to the mountain front is called a pediment surface. A bajada is formed by coalescing alluvial fans. This valley is fault-controlled, that is, a fault runs down the long axis of the valley. It may be a southern extension of the Lake Mead fault zone.

This straight segment of U.S. 95 is on the surface of a broad bajada that extends from the River Mountains into the Eldorado Valley. The Eldorado Mountains are to the east (left) and the Wilson Ridge is beyond, in the far distance in Arizona. The Highland Range is straight ahead and the McCullough Range is to the west (right). The steep rugged mountain just to the west (right) is granite of the Railroad Pass pluton.

3.5 In the late 1970s the Eldorado Valley was still untouched by human activity, except for the high-voltage power lines and a gravel pit. In the 1980s, several industrial and recreational facilities opened in the valley. Factories, a race course, expanded gravel operations, and the new Boulder City airport are several examples of the types of new facilities in the northern part of the valley.

There are plans to build a large solar power plant just south of Boulder City. During the past 10 years, the valley has been considered as the site of a new Las Vegas airport.

3.9 Crossing under the high-voltage power lines that carry electricity from Hoover Dam to the McCullough switching station and then to Phoenix and Los Angeles. Las Vegas receives little power from Hoover Dam.

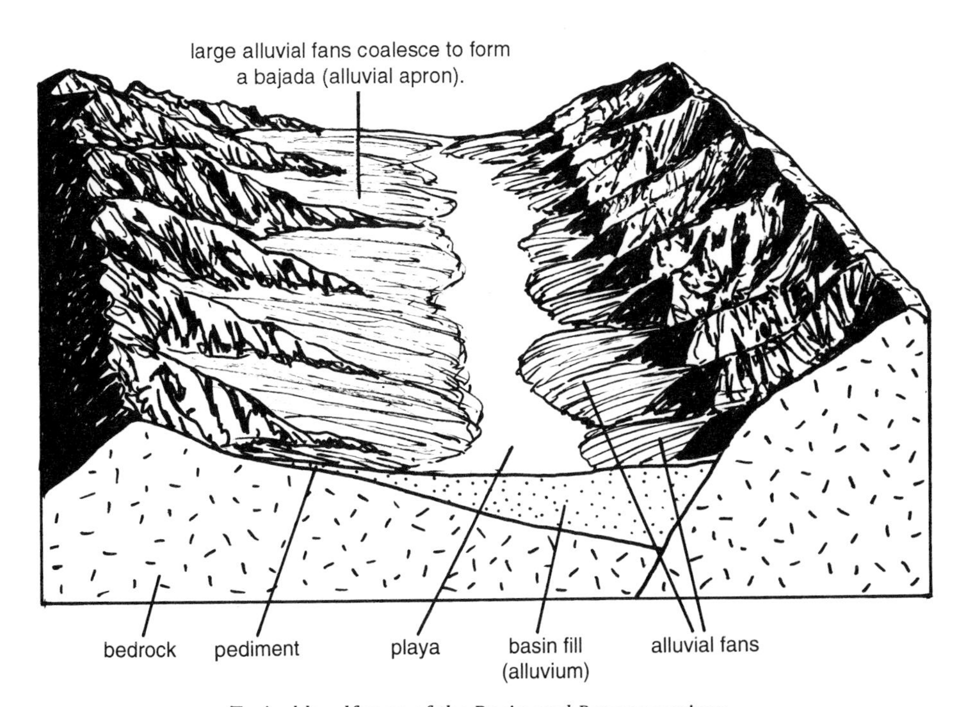

Typical landforms of the Basin and Range province.

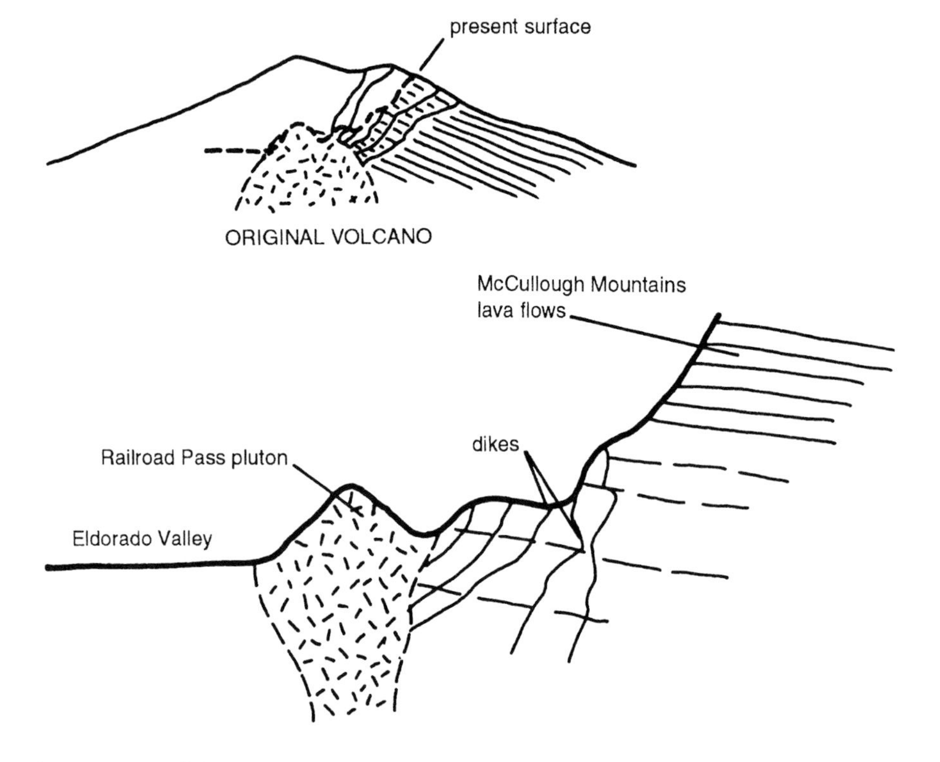

Cross sections of the Miocene McCullough stratovolcano, looking north. The upper diagram shows the stratovolcano in Miocene time, prior to erosion. The lower diagram shows the stratovolcano as it appears today, after 13 to 16 million years of erosion.

4.5 Bands on the mountain to right are the roots of a Miocene stratovolcano. The dark bands are dikes. There is also gold mineralization in the mountain (Blue Quartz mine). On the skyline (right) in the McCullough Range gently tilted lavas may represent the flanks of this volcano. The oldest volcanic flows are about 16 million years old and the youngest about 13 million years old.

5.9 The Eldorado Valley playa is dry during most of the year but, after a major storm, the playa may be filled with several inches of water. The lake has no outlet but the water quickly evaporates in this arid climate, leaving its dissolved salts on the dry lake bed. This is the cycle described in Trip 3 that may form gypsum and other deposits. These ephemeral lakes are the habitat of the long-tailed apus, a shrimp-like crustacean that hatches from microscopic eggs when the lake fills with water. Adults mature quickly–reaching a length of about 2 inches–and lay their eggs before the lake completely dries again. The adults then die and the eggs are scattered by the wind. The eggs can withstand months of dry heat before they are able to hatch with the next rain. This playa is a favorite place to fly model airplanes and ultralight aircraft.

9.0 Volcanoes are especially well exposed in the McCullough Range to the west (right) because there has been little tectonic faulting and tilting. Volcanoes exist in the Eldorado Mountains to the east but have been dissected by numerous faults and tilted (in some areas to nearly 90°). Imagine trying to recognize a volcano that has been tilted on its side.

Eldorado playa (foreground) looking west toward the McCullough Range. Note the layered appearance of the volcanic rocks near the top of the range.

To the west, observe the sequence of Miocene rock layers in the McCullough Range. The dark band at the range summit is andesite of the Hidden Valley volcanics; the white stripe is the McCullough Pass tuff erupted from a caldera in the McCullough Range and below is the Eldorado Valley volcanics. The McCullough Pass tuff (the white band) does not extend to the north. Its flow was stopped by a topographic barrier formed by a large stratovolcano in the northern McCullough Range.

The high southern section of the McCullough Range is composed of Precambrian rock (1.7 billion years old).

10.4 Intersection of U.S. 95 with State Route 165 to Nelson. **Turn left (east) onto State Route 165 to Nelson.**

Note the historical marker at the intersection describing the history of Eldorado Canyon. Written records show that mining began in this area in 1857 in the district of Nelson and has continued intermittently to the present. The total value of mineral production, mostly gold and silver, was 7 to 10 million dollars. Mines in the Eldorado Canyon district have colorful names like Techatticup, Wall Street, and Honest Miner. The district is located near the contact of a large pluton with steeply tilted Miocene volcanic rocks. The gold and silver is found in quartz and calcite veins that cut shattered plutonic rock.

10.7 The road ascends a broad pediment surface that extends from the base of the Eldorado Mountains (ahead and extending to the left) into the north-trending Eldorado Valley.

The small hill to the left is called Bump and is composed of Miocene andesite. In this area, andesite flows are tilted steeply (65° to 90°) to the east and are cut by near horizontal faults.

At 9:00 are the River Mountains, Fortification Hill, and Wilson Ridge (on the skyline).

13.4 The road crosses steeply tilted exposures of andesite lava flows.

14.0 The powerlines overhead carry electricity from Hoover Dam to southern California.

14.6 The andesite flows are tilted steeply to the east.

17.6 The small quarry to the left exposes the tuff of Bridge Spring, a regionally extensive ash-flow sheet that erupted from a source in the Eldorado Mountains about 15.2 million years ago. The exposures are cut by a left-lateral strike-slip fault (such as faults of the Lake Mead fault zone seen in Trip 3) that represents an adjustment or tear fault in the upper plate of a major detachment sheet. This unit is named after Bridge Spring, located about 2 miles north of Nelson and about 1 mile east (left) of State Route 165.

The extension of the crust during Miocene time was originally thought to be accommodated by steep normal faults. G.K. Gilbert, a geologist with the U.S. Geological Survey, proposed this idea in the late 1880s. In 1971, R.E. Anderson, based on work in the Eldorado Mountains near Nelson, suggested that crustal thinning was related to the formation of low-angle normal faults. Low-angle normal faults were recognized earlier (1960) by Chester Longwell, but Anderson's careful and insightful analysis of the rocks in the Eldorado Mountains was critical to demonstrating their importance during crustal extension. A low-angle normal fault that transports rocks a considerable distance is called a detachment fault. Detachment faults place younger rocks in the upper plate over older rocks of the lower plate and are found throughout the Basin and Range province. As is the case in science, there are some geologists who disagree about the importance and even the existence of these faults.

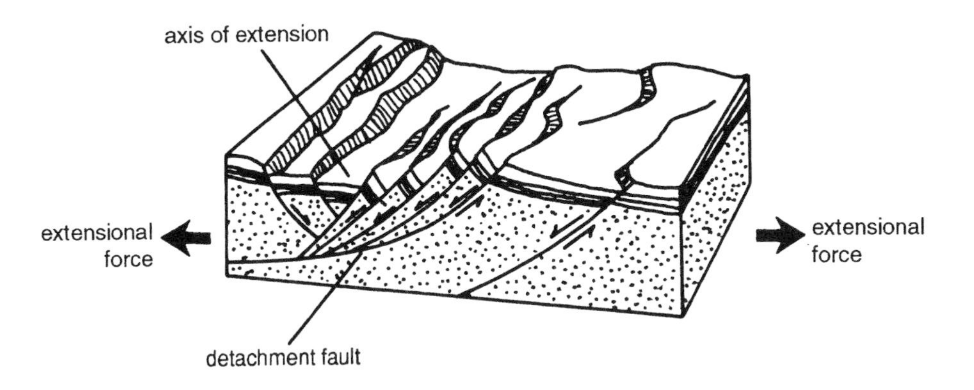

Block diagram of a detachment fault (low-angle normal fault).

Both the Eldorado and McCullough Ranges lie in the upper plate of a detachment fault. The detachment fault may be close to the surface in the Eldorado Mountains causing surface rocks to fault and tilt. The fault may be deep beneath the McCullough Range (to the west) and, as a result, the mountain range is being carried along as an intact block, neither strongly tilted nor faulted.

18.1 The tuff of Bridge Spring forms the jagged cliffs on the skyline to the east (left). The tuff dips about 45° to the east and is underlain by basalt and andesite flows that were erupted between 18.5 and 15.2 million years ago.

18.7 Junction with the Nelson garbage dump road. The tuff of Bridge Spring is cut by numerous north-striking (trending) high angle normal faults that produce a series of west-stepping ridges.

Steeply dipping volcanic rocks in the Eldorado Mountains just north of Nelson.

18.8 The road crosses east-dipping reddish flows of basalt and andesite and interbedded lenses of white volcanic (rhyolite) sandstone.

19.3 The ridge on the right is composed of rhyolite domes and flows. Since the rock layers on the ridge are steeply tilted there are excellent cross sections of volcanic vents displayed on the ridge. Unfortunately, these can only be observed from the air. The rhyolite contains abundant spherulites (spherical masses of radiating feldspar crystals) which weather from the rock face and accumulate below.

19.6 To the east (left) a dacite dike cuts across exposures of basalt and andesite flows and the tuff of Bridge Spring.

20.2 The route begins descending into Nelson. Steeply tilted lavas and tuff of Bridge Spring are on the left. Exposures of rhyolite are to the right.

21.2 Entering Nelson. Nelson was the center of one of the oldest mining districts in Nevada, known today as the Eldorado district. Other names for this district were Nelson and Colorado. Gold was discovered in Eldorado Canyon some time in the 1700s by the Spanish exploring the Colorado River, but the Mohave Indians were hostile and mining never progressed. Arrastres and prospect holes left from the Spanish activity were found later, around 1857, when gold was rediscovered on the Honest Miner claim. The district was organized in 1861 while it was still part of New Mexico Territory. The mines produced most of the district's total production in gold, silver, copper, lead, and zinc between 1864 and 1900 from veins in quartz monzonite. The Techatticup mine was the largest producer in the

Photo looking east at the old mining town of Nelson (middleground). Photo courtesy of the California Division of Mines and Geology.

The Southwestern Mining Company at the mouth of Eldorado Canyon on the shore of the Colorado River, in about 1890. (Photo courtesy of the Nevada Historical Society.)

district producing more than $3,500,000 between 1860 and 1900, and about $1,117,200 from 1900 to 1930. The name *techatticup* may come from the Southern Paiute words *tecahenga* (hungry) and *tosoup* (flour) combined to mean "hungry, come and eat some flour." It may also mean "enough for everybody," "plenty for all," or "white flower." Many mine shafts, adits, and drifts honeycomb the surrounding hills. Large stamp mills used to operate near the mines and at the mouth of Eldorado Canyon on the Colorado River.

State Route 165 continues to the east (left) and begins a long descent through Eldorado Canyon which includes several washes in its drainage, including Techatticup Wash. Volcanic rocks are to the left and the Nelson pluton is on the right.

The word *Eldorado* first appears in the early sixteenth century as the Spanish name for a legendary Indian chief of Bogota. It means "the gilded one."

22.6 Teddy Bear cholla cactus "forest" on both sides of the road (see color photo on page 28).

22.8 Crossing over the Welcome fault, which places the tuff of Bridge Spring against older volcanic rocks.

23.4 The Techatticup mine is on the right.

24.4 The route now crosses the Eldorado fault. This structure places volcanic rocks against metamorphic rocks of Precambrian age. The

Eldorado fault may be the master structure (detachment fault) in the Eldorado Mountains. The high-angle normal and strike-slip faults seen north of Nelson lie in the hanging wall (upper plate) of this fault.

25.0 Entering Lake Mead National Recreation Area.

26.1 Lake Mohave appears ahead. The Colorado River widens here due to the damming of its waters about 45 miles to the south at Davis Dam in Laughlin.

26.4 Conglomerates representing debris shed in alluvial fans from the Eldorado Mountains are banked against Precambrian bedrock to the south (right) of the road. For perhaps tens of thousands of years during the wetter Pleistocene epoch, boulders, gravel, and sand were deposited here as muddy debris flows. Note the beautifully developed erosional spires in the gravels of Techatticup Wash (see color photo on page 28). Similar landforms of similar age can be seen in Kyle Canyon on Trip 2.

27.3 Excellent views of gravel deposits in Techatticup Wash. Fire Mountain is to the east across Lake Mohave. The Fire Mountain area may be part of a major volcano, the source for many lava flows in the region.

28.8 A paved road descends into Techatticup Wash to the former site of the small recreational settlement of Nelsons Landing Marina and Resort.

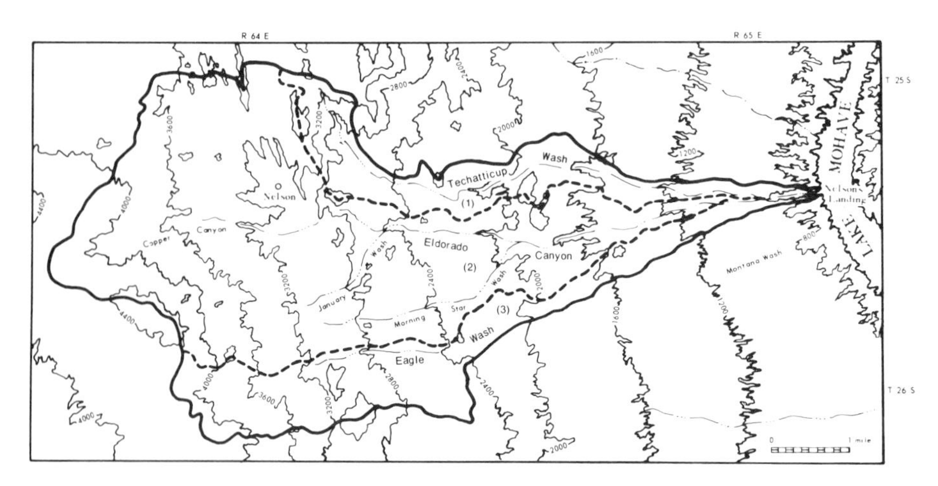

The Eldorado drainage basin is composed of three sub-basins: Techatticup basin, Eldorado Canyon basin proper, and Eagle basin. These sub-basins combine into one narrow channel a short distance west of the community of Nelsons Landing, causing concentration of runoff. Courtesy of California Division of Mines and Geology and U.S. Geological Survey.)

Walls of resistant sandstone form a narrow slot through which the entire runoff from a 22 square mile drainage area flashed, demolishing Nelsons Landing. The Eldorado Mountains are in the background. Photo courtesy of the California Division of Mines and Geology.

Flash floods and accompanying mud and debris flows are common in desert regions, and this settlement was destroyed by such an occurrence in October 1974. Nine people died. The storm that brought the rain was an unusual cloudburst that originated over Eldorado Valley and moved southeast to Nelson. In one hour it provided half the annual precipitation for this area. Waters from Eagle and Techatticup Washes joined those of Eldorado Canyon in a narrow channel only a few thousand feet west of Nelsons Landing.

Damaged mobile homes, which were parked near the bottom of Eldorado Canyon when the flood swept through, were a total loss. In all, about 31 homes were damaged or carried out into Lake Mohave and lost. Photo courtesy of the California Division of Mines and Geology.

The floodwater reached a maximum depth of 20 to 30 feet at the narrowest point in the channel (about 100 feet wide) and carried mostly gravel-sized debris and a few boulders up to 4 feet in diameter. This rock debris formed deposits at least 12 feet thick at the mouth of the canyon. Most of the town was carried into Lake Mohave.

A geologist reading the rocks along the sides of the canyon, where there is cemented debris from many past floods, would have known that this would be a prime location for such an event. Indeed, a year prior to this flood, the National Park Service had warned the inhabitants of Nelsons Landing of the danger of living in this narrow canyon.

At Nelsons Landing; well-cemented blocks of sandstone that caved off the canyon walls have covered and preserved gravel and boulder debris of past floods. Subsequent flood waters have banked up younger debris against these blocks on their upstream side (right of photo). Much geologic evidence here and in other parts of Eldorado Canyon suggests a long history of flooding. Photo courtesy of the California Division of Mines and Geology.

29.0 Loop at the end of State Route 165. Stop and view Lake Mohave. This area is a popular fishing spot. Several poorly marked (and possibly dangerous) trails lead down to the lake from this area. They are not recommended.

Retrace State Route 165 back to the intersection with U.S. 95. Turn right on U.S. 95 toward Henderson and Boulder City.

0.0 **At the intersection of U.S. 95 and the Boulder Highway (U.S. 93/95), turn left toward Henderson and set odometer to 0.0.**

0.9 The Alunite (or Railroad Pass) mining district is located on both sides of the road. This district, established in 1907, contains small amounts of disseminated gold and silver in volcanic rock altered to a potassium-aluminum-rich mineral called alunite. In 1917 and again during World War II, there was considerable interest in the mining of alunite as a source of potash and alumina, but the purity and distribution of the ore was unfavorable for commercial exploitation.

1.5 The Railroad Pass Hotel and Casino is on the right.

The cliff above the casino is composed of andesitic lava and ash-flow tuff. The location of the volcano that erupted these units is a mystery because this volcanic section is separated from all other volcanic units by faults. An important northwest trending normal fault is exposed just below the casino water tank. This fault separates mineralized rock (east) from unmineralized rock (west).

Horizontal openings that miners drill and blast into mountains in search of ore are called adits. Several adits are visible in this area. Adits and related mine workings in this area penetrate the mountain as far as 500 feet. These workings are very dangerous. State law requires that open shafts be marked and fenced, but it is prudent to stay away from open shafts and take care when exploring in mining districts.

2.0 Railroad crossing. This railroad served as the main supply route to Hoover Dam during its construction. The tracks are no longer used, but plans to run a tourist train from Boulder City to Henderson through Railroad Pass have been proposed.

2.4 Crossing Railroad Pass (elevation 2,373 feet). Straight ahead is a beautiful view of Las Vegas Valley. The view is especially spectacular at night. Beyond Las Vegas Valley to the north lie the Sheep and Las Vegas Ranges, which form the northern boundary of the valley.

The TV towers at 9:00 are located on Black Mountain at the northern tip of the McCullough Range. Black Mountain is composed of a thick dacite lava flow that overlies thin flows of andesite—remnants of a Miocene stratovolcano. The oldest volcanic flows are about 16 million years old and the youngest about 13 million years old.

The northern McCullough Range contains many petroglyph sites, mostly in hard-to-find canyons. The early inhabitants may have spent the summer months in the mountains to escape the heat of Las Vegas Valley, but they were still close enough to take advantage of abundant water that at one time existed in the valley.

The River Mountains, to the left of the highway (east), are composed of tilted and faulted andesite and dacite lavas (refer to mile 5.6 on page 100 for a description of the geology of this range).

Clark County Heritage Museum.

3.8 I-515 intersection.

4.9 The Clark County Heritage Museum is on the right. Take time to stop. This museum offers realistic exhibits of the natural and historical highlights of this area. The displays change to highlight various topics and the bookstore carries a top line of informational books and gifts relating to this part of Nevada.

10.1 Intersection of Lake Mead Drive and Boulder Highway in Henderson.

End of trip.

TRIP 5—YOUNG FAULT SCARPS AND SUBSIDENCE IN LAS VEGAS VALLEY

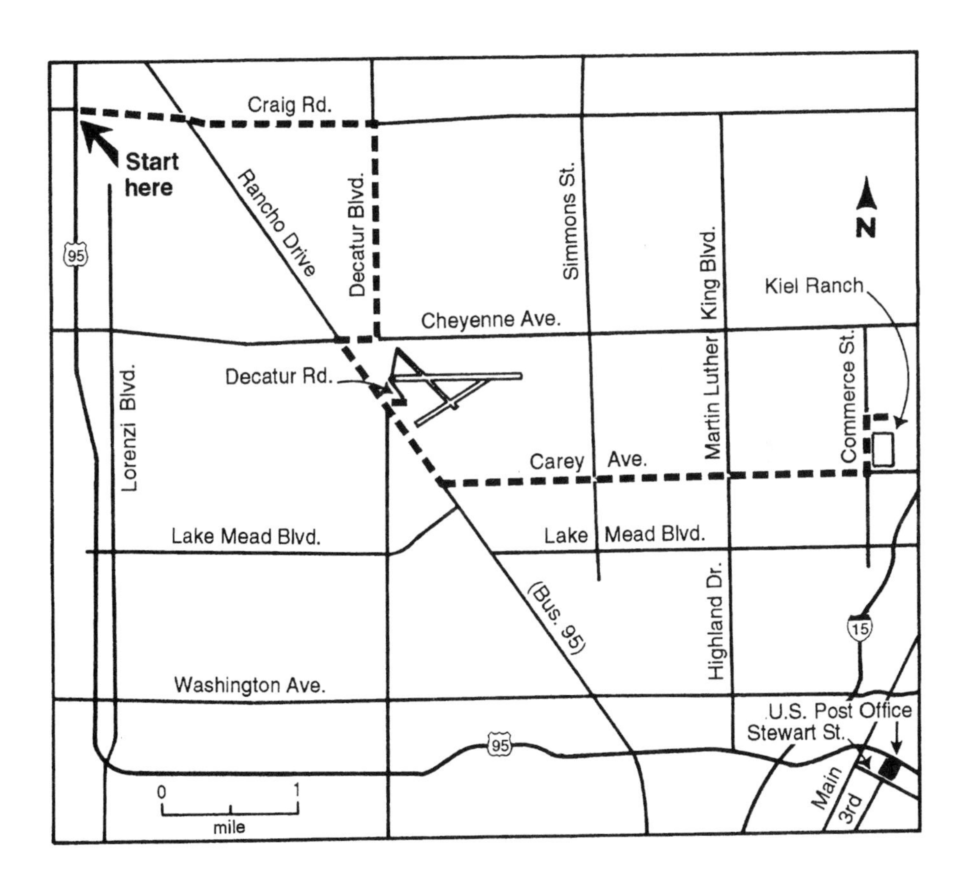

This short 9-mile trip focuses on the north-central part of Las Vegas Valley and recent geologic features that are especially critical to property owners in this area. Movement along faults that produced earthquakes, fractures that have caused millions of dollars in damage as a result of over-pumping of groundwater, and the effects of land subsidence due to groundwater withdrawal can be observed along this route. In addition, one of the historic spring areas in Las Vegas will be visited.

0.0 **Begin this trip at the intersection of U.S. 95 and Craig Road. Set odometer to 0.0.** Drive east on Craig Road. (*Note*: To get to the intersection from downtown Las Vegas, drive 9.4 miles north on U.S. 95 from I-15.)

0.9 Intersection with Rancho Drive. Continue east on Craig Road.

1.1 Cross a small fault scarp (a subtle, downward step or bend) in the road. This is the first of a series of scarps that cross Craig Road and mark the surface locations of faults that cut the alluvial sediments that fill Las Vegas Valley.

1.6 Cross another scarp. You can stop at the curb on the right side of the road to view the scarp just ahead. When rock masses are stressed due to forces operating in the Earth's crust and the stress exceeds the rock's ability to stay in one piece, the rock fails or breaks and moves in whatever direction it can to relieve the stress. The movement of rock along a break or fault causes an earthquake. The plane along which the rocks move is called a fault. Erosion gradually smooths the faulted or broken surface to form a gentle scarp in the surface that slopes, in this case, to the east.

These faults are interesting because they are sites of past and possibly future earthquakes. There are a number of active or potentially active faults in and near Las Vegas Valley. Earthquakes of magnitude 3 or smaller are fairly common and generally cause no damage.

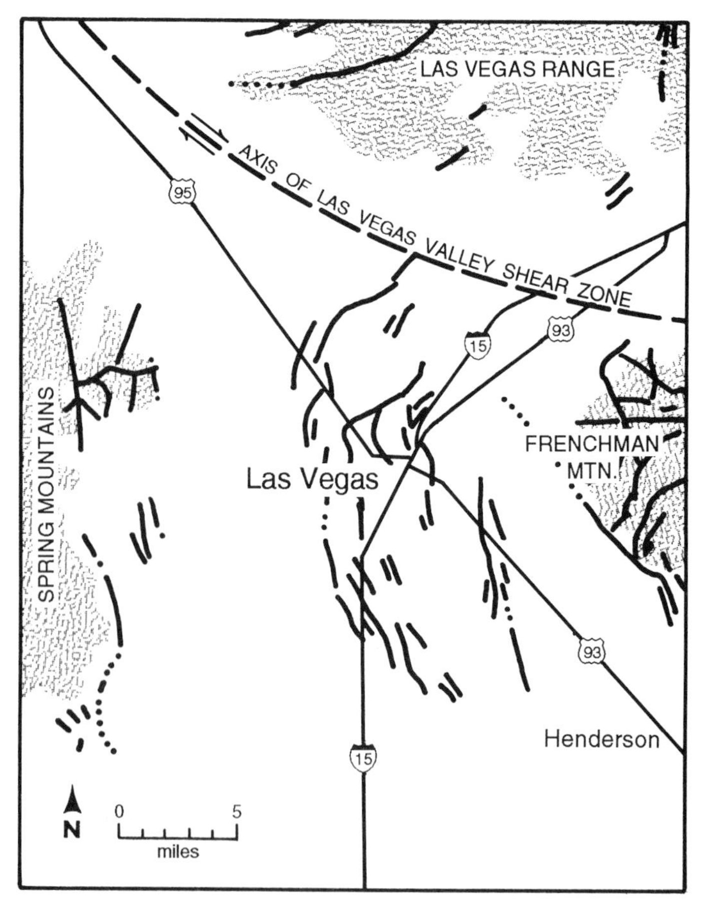

Major faults in and near Las Vegas Valley.

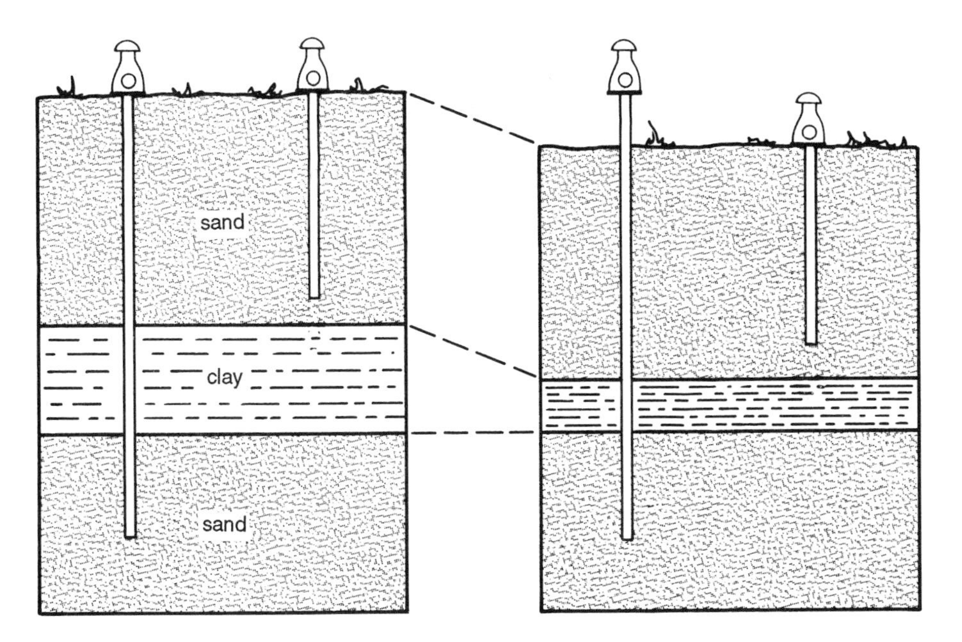

Wellhead protrusion resulting from compression of soil layers due to groundwater withdrawal (after Mindling, 1965). Wells that do not penetrate the compressed layer are not affected.

Significant earthquakes, of magnitude 6 or greater, are much less frequent, and may occur on a given fault only once every few thousand years.

These faults are also preferred sites for cracks to develop in response to pumping groundwater. For decades, municipal and private water wells have pumped more water from the ground than is naturally returned by precipitation of rain and snow in the mountains. This over-pumping results in several phenomena that can cause problems. One is land subsidence. Water can normally be drawn from compacted sand or sandstone aquifers without subsidence, but when clays occur in the sediments, as they do in the central and eastern part of the valley, pumping water causes the clays to compress and the overlying land surface to sink.

Downtown Las Vegas has actually dropped in elevation by more than 5 feet since 1935, when geodetic monitoring in the valley was begun. Much of the valley is sinking at a relatively uniform rate so that most structures are not adversely affected. Locally, however, the subsidence is focussed on preexisting geologic faults, which serve as points of weakness for ground movement. Geodetic control lines placed for ten years (1978–1987) over several selected faults in areas of high subsidence revealed movement of as much as 2 inches per year on several of the faults.

Land subsidence in Las Vegas Valley can be attributed to tectonic activity, natural prehistoric dewatering of the basin sediments,

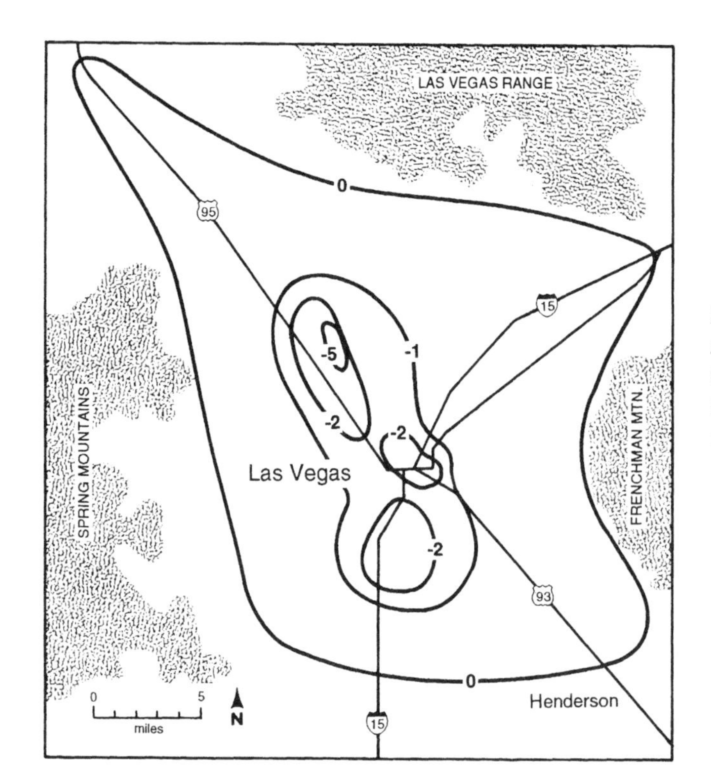

Land surface subsidence (in feet) in Las Vegas Valley between 1963 and 1987.

increased loading from the weight of Lake Mead (Longwell's measurements from 1935 to 1950 show that the impounded waters have caused a depression of about 7 inches centered on the lake and 4-5 inches of tilting of the Las Vegas Valley), and historic groundwater extraction. Of these potential causes, man's influence on the groundwater system is, without a doubt, the most important and immediate factor.

In the absence of geodetically controlled leveling data, subsidence-induced movement on the faults can be detected by the development of cracks or fissures in the ground that form on or in close proximity to the faults. The fissures begin as hairline cracks, then are widened by surface water that erodes the walls of the crack. These thin cracks are deep. They originate at depths of perhaps tens of feet and migrate upward with time. Finally they cut the land surface. Some fissures are hundreds to thousands of feet long and are widened by erosion at the surface to as much as several feet.

Houses built over these cracks and subsequent erosion gullies can be severely damaged; foundations crack and tilt into holes. As much as $12 million in damage has occurred in one subdivision in North Las Vegas. Most of the fissures that have developed in Las Vegas Valley occur near faults (within 1,200 feet). Ways to avoid this geological hazard after the crack reaches the surface include not

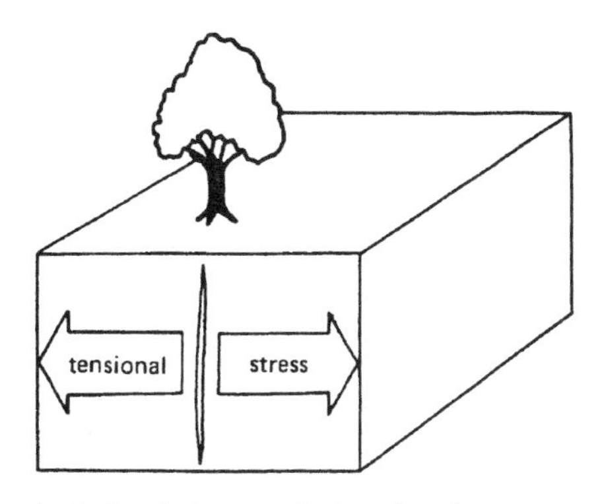

1. Lateral stresses induce tension cracking.

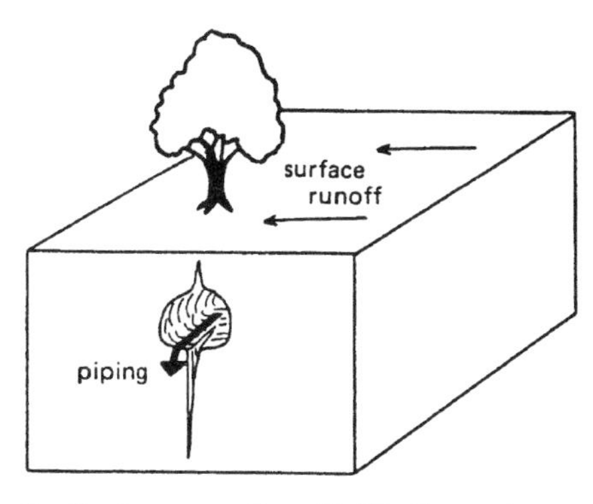

2. Surface runoff and infiltration enlarge crack through subsurface piping.

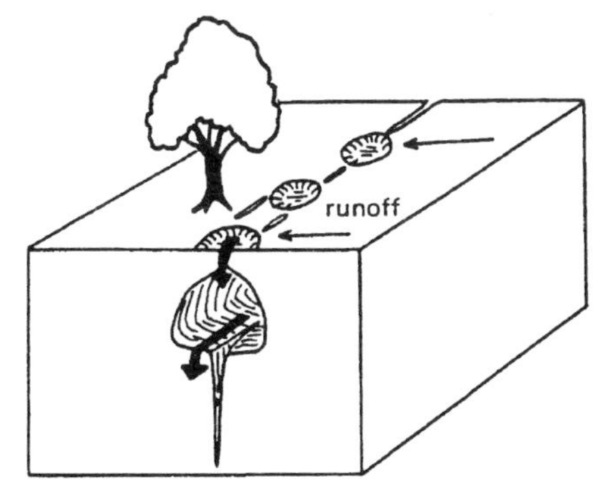

3. As piping continues, the fissure begins to appear at surface as series of potholes and small cracks.

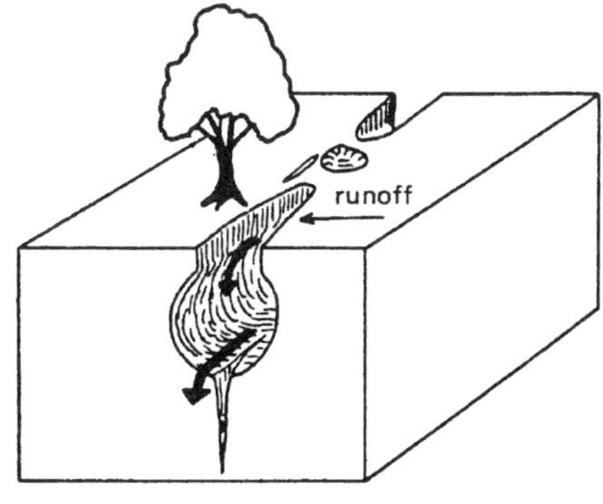

4. As infiltration and erosion continue, the fissure enlarges and completely opens to the surface as the tunnel roof collapses.

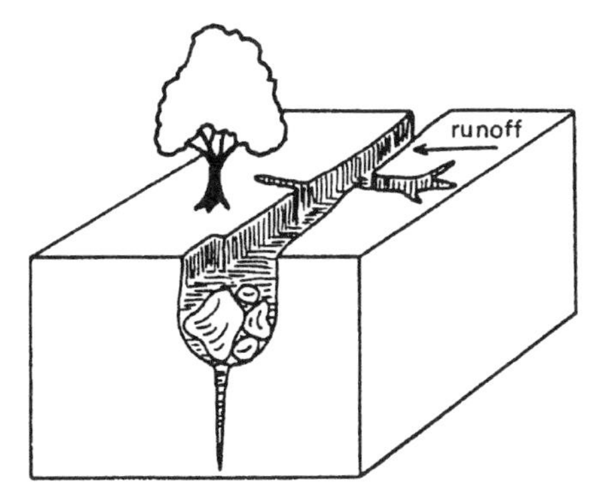

5. The entire fissure is opened to the surface and enlargement continues as the fissure walls are widened; extensive slumping and side-stream gullying occur.

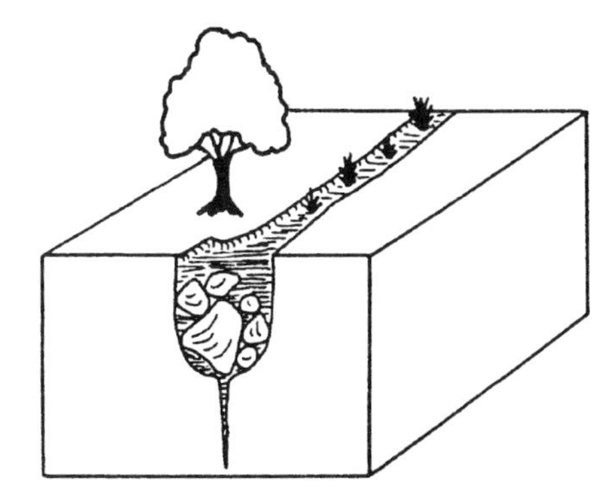

6. The fissure becomes filled with slump and runoff debris and is marked by a line of vegetation and slight surface depression.

Development of fissures (after Bell, 1981).

building over known fissures or near faults, limiting irrigation in the areas of known fissures, and channeling rain and irrigation waters away from fissures.

Fissure, widened by erosion, running beneath the foundation of an abandoned home near Simmons Street in North Las Vegas.

In recent years the Las Vegas Valley Water District, the major water supplier in the valley, has been artificially recharging and discharging the aquifers at depth. Colorado River water (from Lake Mead) is injected into the ground during the winter months, then pumped back out during the high-demand summer months for irrigation of lawns and golf courses. Time and research will disclose what effect this repeated recharge and discharge to the aquifers will have on subsidence, fissure development, and movement along recent faults in the valley.

2.2 Turn right (south) onto Decatur Boulevard.

3.7 Turn right (west) onto Cheyenne Avenue.

3.9 Turn left (southeast) onto Rancho Drive.

4.6 Turn left (northeast) onto Decatur Drive, into the parking lot at the North Las Vegas Air Terminal. Just inside the parking area, look to the right. Behind a chain-link fence is a water well. The cement pad around this well has been broken by land subsidence. The well, with its steel casing, more or less remained in place when all the ground around it sank. Although Las Vegas now gets the bulk of its water from the Colorado River—a result of the formation of the Southern Nevada Water Project established in the 1970s—wells still provide approximately 20 to 30 percent of the water needs in the valley.

0.0 **Reset odometer to 0.0, then turn left (southeast) onto Rancho Drive.**

0.7 Turn left (east) onto Carey Avenue.

1.6 Pass the Carey Lake Detention Basin on the right. This man-made lake was built to control flash floods. Although Las Vegas Valley has an average annual precipitation of only 4 inches per year, individual storms can dump as much as 2 inches in brief periods of time in parts of the valley.

1.9 Continue straight on Carey Avenue at the intersection of Simmons Street. Numerous fissures occur in this area.

2.2 One fissure runs from the left side of the road into the playground at Gilbert Elementary School on the left. Several homes on the small hill behind the school have been damaged by fissures. The hill itself is a fault scarp.

3.7 Carey Avenue crosses another fault scarp.

3.8 Turn left (north) onto Commerce Street.

Las Vegas Spring, about 1900. Photo courtesy of the Nevada Historical Society.

3.9 Turn right onto the gravel road. Drive another 0.1 mile to the well at the Kiel Ranch Historic Site. The ranch house burned to the ground in August 1992, but take a walk around the trees and down to the grassy low spot. This is the site of one of the historical natural springs around which Las Vegas grew. Las Vegas is Spanish for *The Meadows*. The soil around the low spot is colored gray from numerous campfires of the many people who used these springs. Following the aboriginal Indians, the Spaniards visited these watering places as early as 1770. John Frémont camped here during his expedition in 1844.

The first pumping of groundwater logically occurred near the historic natural springs. The main well field of the Las Vegas Valley Water District, near the intersection of Charleston and Valley View Boulevards, is located at the site of the valley's historic lush meadows. Pumping of groundwater here since the mid-1930s has progressively lowered the water table, such that the natural springs no longer flow.

Rain and snow precipitated in the higher mountains bordering the valley on the north and west provide most of the groundwater that slowly flows underground through sediments that fill Las Vegas Valley. Most flow occurs through pore space in layers of sandy sediments. These sand or sandstone aquifers are separated by layers of

The wellhead at Well No. 5 at Las Vegas Valley Water District's main well field is more than 4 feet above the land surface because of subsidence caused by groundwater withdrawal. Photo by John Bell.

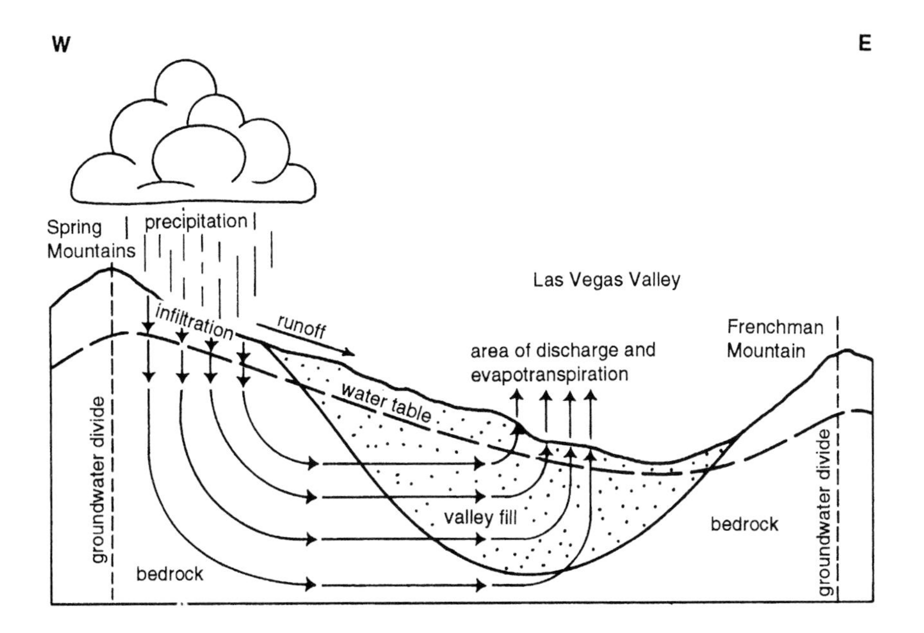

Generalized groundwater flow system in Las Vegas Valley (after Domenico and others, 1964).

very fine-grained clay. The clay layers slow the penetration of rain water vertically into the ground.

In contrast, most of the rain that falls in the valley does not reach the water table; some runs off into ephemeral streams and much evaporates into the atmosphere.

To get back to downtown Las Vegas, return to Commerce Street. Turn left (south) and drive 0.1 mile on Commerce Street to Carey Avenue. Turn left (east) and drive 0.1 mile on Carey Avenue to Losee Road. Turn right and drive 0.5 mile on Losee Road to Lake Mead Boulevard. Turn left (east) on Lake Mead Boulevard. Drive 0.1 mile to I-15. Take I-15 southwest toward downtown Las Vegas and the Strip.

Optional Stop—Survey benchmark on the right (southeast) side of the steps of the U.S. Post Office at the intersection of Stewart Avenue and Third Street in downtown Las Vegas. This benchmark is within walking distance of hotels in downtown Las Vegas. The benchmark was surveyed in 1936. Since that time, the benchmark, the Post Office and the surrounding land have subsided about 5 feet relative to presumably stable benchmarks in bedrock in the mountain ranges.

Until recently, surveying benchmarks was tedious work that required the use of transits or other telescope-type instruments and tape measures.

The development of lasers eliminated tape measures; laser surveying instruments calculate the distance by measuring the time that it takes the light to travel between stations.

The most recent advance in surveying is the deployment of the Global Positioning System (GPS) satellites by the U.S. Department of Defense. A receiver on the ground picks up a signal from each satellite overhead. Precise clocks in the satellites allow measurement of the distance from the satellite to the ground (again, by measuring time and calculating distance from the speed of light or radio signals). By using two receivers, precise locations can be calculated to within fractions of an inch. The Nevada Bureau of Mines and Geology uses GPS receivers to measure continuing subsidence in Las Vegas Valley. The Department of Defense developed GPS for military uses, such as locating ships at sea and infantry in featureless deserts, and directing smart bombs and missiles.

End of trip.

Glossary

adit A horizontal or nearly horizontal passage from the surface into a mine.
agglomerate A pyroclastic rock containing a predominance of rounded or subangular fragments greater than 32 mm.
alluvial Pertaining to alluvium.
alluvial fan A fan-shaped deposit of alluvium typically built where a stream leaves a steep mountain valley and runs out onto a level plain or meets a slower stream.
alluvium Sediment deposited by streams in nonmarine environments, including river beds, flood plains, lakes, fans at the base of mountain slopes, and estuaries.
altered Said of a rock that has undergone a change in its mineralogical composition, that is typically brought about by the action of hydrothermal solutions.
alumina Aluminum oxide.
alunite A mineral (hydrated potassium aluminum sulfate), found usually in soft white, gray, or pink masses in hydrothermally altered rocks that originally contained abundant feldspar.
andesite A fine-grained volcanic rock that solidifies from molten lava at the Earth's surface. It is intermediate in composition between basalt and rhyolite, and ranges in color from dark gray-green, lighter gray, red or brown.
anhydrite An evaporite mineral (anhydrous calcium sulfate) commonly found with gypsum in massive beds. It is translucent with glassy to pearly luster, and generally white or gray.
anticline An arching fold in which the limbs dip away from the axis. The oldest rocks occur at the center of the fold, with progressively younger rocks found outward from the core.
ash, volcanic Fine pyroclastic material produced by the explosive emission of hot, gas-charged lava from a volcanic crater or fissure that cools on its descent to the ground. It consists of fragments mostly under 4 mm in diameter and is usually light gray.
ash-flow tuff Volcanic rock composed of formerly hot, gas-charged volcanic ash that flowed down the side of a volcano.
asthenosphere The weak, plastic, partly molten layer of the upper mantle directly below the lithosphere. It lies at a depth of 100 to 350 km below the Earth's surface.
badlands A region nearly devoid of vegetation where erosion has cut into easily erodible rock forming an intricate maze of narrow ravines and sharp crests and pinnacles. Travel across such a landscape is almost impossible, hence the name.
bajada A series of coalescing alluvial fans along the base of a mountain range.
barite A mineral, barium sulfate, and the principal ore of barium.
basalt A fine-grained igneous rock that solidifies from molten lava at the Earth's surface. It is usually black, due to the predominance of the minerals calcic plagioclase, olivine, and pyroxene, along with other dark-colored accessory minerals.
basement The undifferentiated complex of rocks (generally igneous or metamorphic) that underlie the rocks of interest in an area.
Basin and Range province A physiographic region in the western United States that consists of fault-block mountains and intervening sediment-filled basins.
basin-and-range extension Extension, or pulling apart, of the crust of the Earth in the western United States has produced the present physiography of generally north-trending mountain ranges separated by intervening sediment-filled basins.
batholith A large body of intrusive igneous (plutonic) rock, often produced by multiple intrusions.

bedding Depositional layers or planes dividing sedimentary rocks of the same or different lithology.

bedrock Any solid rock exposed at the Earth's surface or overlain by unconsolidated material.

biotite A common rock-forming mineral and a member of the mica group of minerals. It ranges from dark brown to green and exhibits perfect basal cleavage, that is, it will peel into thin, transparent layers along one plane.

bleaching A lightening of the original color of rock; a surface effect caused by long exposure to weathering or a more penetrating effect caused when circulating solutions, generally hot, have altered the original chemical composition of the minerals forming the rocks.

borax A mineral (hydrous sodium borate). An ore of boron.

breccia A coarse-grained rock composed of angular fragments of broken rock in a finer-grained matrix; may or may not be cemented.

butte A conspicuous isolated hill or small mountain with very steep sides, a small mesa.

caldera A large, bowl-shaped volcanic depression with a diameter many times greater than the included volcanic vent or vents. It may be formed by explosion or collapse.

calcite Calcium carbonate, the principal constituent of limestone.

caliche A solid, almost impervious accumulation of whitish calcarious material commonly found in layers on or near the surface of soils in arid regions.

cap rock A hard rock layer capping a softer rock unit (such as basalt capping a soft sandstone).

carbonate rock A rock consisting mainly of carbonate minerals, such as limestone or dolostone.

chert A sedimentary rock composed of extremely fine-grained quartz, formed by organic or inorganic precipitation or by replacement. Flint is a variety of chert.

cinder, volcanic Uncemented, glassy, vesicular rock ejected from a volcanic vent.

cinder cone A conical hill formed by the accumulation of volcanic ash or cinders around a vent.

clast A piece of broken rock or an individual constituent of sedimentary rock produced by the physical disintegration of a larger rock mass.

clay 1. An extremely fine-grained, natural sediment or soft rock composed of clay-sized (less than 4 microns) particles. 2. A group of silicate minerals.

colemanite A mineral (hydrous calcium borate) that is colorless to white, transparent to translucent, with a glassy luster.

compressional deformation Structural deformation of rocks due to compressive (squeezing) forces within the Earth's crust.

concretion A hard, nodular body enclosed in a softer sedimentary rock and consisting of a substance precipitated from solution.

conglomerate A sedimentary rock consisting of rounded rock fragments, over 2 mm in diameter, set in a finer-grained matrix.

contact The place or surface where two different kinds of rocks come together.

continental plate A thick portion of the Earth's crust that comprises a continent.

corrasion Erosion of rock and soil by the abrasive action of particles set in motion by running water, wind, glaciers, or gravity.

cross-bedding A sequence of beds inclined at an angle to the main bedding planes in granular sediments. In plan view, the inclined beds are at right-angles to the direction of the wind or water current that deposited them.

crust The outermost compositional shell of the Earth, 10 to 40 kilometers thick, consisting predominantly of relatively low density silicate rocks.

crustal extension Separation, or pulling apart, of the Earth's crust due to forces in the lower crust and mantle, such as convection currents, which are believed to "drive" the continental and oceanic plates of the Earth's crust.
dacite A light-colored volcanic rock about midway between andesite and rhyolite in mineralogical composition and appearance.
debris flow The downslope movement of a mass of unconsolidated and unsorted rock with associated water and mud.
detachment fault A large-scale low-angle or thrust fault.
detrital Clastic. Consisting of fragments of rocks that have been moved individually from their places of origin.
differential weathering Weathering that occurs at different rates or intensity as a result of variations in the composition and structure of rocks.
dike A tabular sheet of intrusive igneous rock that cuts across the structure of the intruded rock or cuts massive rock.
dip The angle in degrees between the horizontal and an inclined geologic plane, such as a bedding plane or a fault. Dip is measured in a plane that is perpendicular to the intersection of the plane with the horizontal.
dip slope A slope of the land surface that conforms approximately to the dip of the underlying rocks.
dissected Cut by erosion into hills and valleys.
dissolution The chemical weathering process whereby minerals and rock material pass directly into solution.
dolomite A mineral, calcium magnesium carbonate. It has a glassy or pearly luster and is usually some shade of gray, tan, or pink.
dolostone A sedimentary rock composed of fragmental, replacement, or precipitated dolomite of organic or inorganic origin.
dome A smoothly rounded, rock-capped mountain, roughly resembling the dome or cupola of a building.
ephemeral stream A stream that flows only occasionally in direct response to precipitation.
erosion The group of related processes by which rock is broken down physically and chemically and the products removed from any part of the earth's surface. It includes the processes of weathering, solution, corrasion, and transportation.
evaporite A mineral deposit formed by the evaporation of water in a restricted basin; also, the minerals of such deposits.
extension In geology, horizontal expansion or pulling apart of the earth.
extensional deformation The deformation rocks undergo when subjected to extension, generally consisting of low- to high-angle faulting.
extrusive Volcanic. Applies to those igneous rocks derived from magmas or magmatic materials that are poured out or ejected onto the Earth's surface.
fault A fracture or planar break in rock (which may be a few inches or many miles long) along which there is movement of one side relative to the other.
fault breccia Crushed and broken rock adjacent to a fault formed by the mechanical breakup of rocks during displacement along it.
fault gouge Finely abraded material occurring between the walls of a fault, the result of grinding during movement.
fault surface The surface along which dislocation has taken place along a fault.
fault trace The line of intersection of a fault plane with the Earth's surface.
fault zone A fault, instead of being a single clean fracture, may be a zone as much as hundreds or even thousands of feet wide; the fault zone consists of numerous interlacing small faults or a complex zone of fault gouge or breccia.
fissure A extensional crack, break, or fracture in the rocks.

flash flood A local, sudden flood of water through a stream channel, generally of relatively great volume and short duration after intense local precipitation.

formation A distinctive, mappable rock unit representing deposition under a uniform set of conditions and at one time.

gneiss A coarse-grained metamorphic rock exhibiting a banded texture (foliation). Bands rich in granular minerals alternate with bands of flaky or elongate minerals.

granite A coarse-grained, plutonic rock containing the minerals quartz and orthoclase, with lesser amounts of plagioclase feldspar, mica, and hornblende as the mafic (dark colored) minerals. The presence of mica and feldspar commonly give granite a salt and pepper appearance.

granodiorite A coarse-grained, plutonic rock resembling granite and consisting of quartz, plagioclase, and orthoclase feldspar, with lesser amounts of biotite mica, hornblende, or pyroxene as the mafic (dark colored) minerals.

gypsum A mineral, hydrous calcium sulfate, that is common in evaporite deposits, and is used to make plaster and wallboard.

hematite A metallic mineral (iron oxide) that is reddish brown to black or silver gray. An important ore of iron.

hornblende A common rock-forming dark silicate mineral with a complex chemical formula.

igneous rock Rock formed by the cooling and consolidation of magma.

intrusive Plutonic. Magma that penetrated into or between other rocks and solidified before reaching the Earth's surface.

kaolinite A clay mineral (hydrous aluminum silicate) that exhibits a dull to pearly luster, and is usually white, but may be variously colored by impurities.

landslide A general term covering a variety of rapid, mass movement processes downslope on the earth's surface.

lava flow Magma that flows out at the Earth's surface.

lava shield A shield volcano. A volcano with a low, flat, broad shape, formed by the buildup of many thin lava flows.

left-lateral fault A strike-slip fault in which relative motion is such that to an observer looking directly at (perpendicular to) the fault, the motion of the block on the opposite side of the fault is to the left.

life zone A zone defined by elevation and/or latitude that hosts a characteristic assemblage of flora.

limestone A sedimentary rock consisting chiefly of calcium carbonate, mainly in the form of the mineral calcite.

lithology The description of compositional and physical characteristics of a rock, generally as determined megascopically or with the aid of a low-power magnifier.

lithosphere The rigid, outermost layer of the Earth, 50 to 100 km thick, encompassing the crust and upper mantle.

low-angle normal fault A gently inclined, dip-slip fault in which the hanging wall has moved downward relative to the footwall.

lower plate The footwall or lower side of an inclined fault.

mafic A dark-colored rock, magma, or mineral rich in iron and magnesium.

magma Molten rock, together with any suspended crystals and dissolved gases, that is generated when temperatures rise and melting occurs in the mantle or crust. Igneous rocks are formed when magma cools and consolidates.

magma chamber A large reservoir in the Earth's crust occupied by magma.

magmatic Of, pertaining to, or derived from magma.

manganite A metallic mineral formed of manganese and oxygen and hydrogen. It is characteristically opaque, steel-gray to black, and has long, prismatic crystals.

mass-wasting The downslope movement of loose surface rock and soil material under the influence of gravity, and without other mediums of transport.

mesa A tableland; a flat-topped mountain or other elevated landform bounded on at least one side by a steep cliff.

metamorphic rock Rock whose original textures or mineral components, or both, have been transformed to new textures and components as a result of high temperature, high pressure, or both.

microcline A feldspar mineral (calcium aluminum silicate) that exhibits a glassy luster, is transparent to translucent, and varies from white to pale yellow, or pink. Green microcline in known as Amazon stone.

mineral A naturally occurring, inorganic, solid element or compound, with a definite composition or compositional range and a regular internal crystal structure.

monzonite A granular plutonic rock resembling granite that contains approximately equal amounts of orthoclase and plagioclase (feldspars). Quartz is usually present in very minor quantities (less than 2% of the volume of the rock). Biotite and hornblende are usually present, along with lesser amounts of apatite, zircon, and sphene.

normal fault An inclined fault along which the upper side has moved downward relative to the lower side.

oceanic plate The crustal plate that underlies an ocean.

orthoclase A mineral (potassium aluminum silicate), a member of the feldspar group and a common mineral in granitic rocks. Its luster is glassy, and it ranges from colorless, to white, to gray, to flesh-red.

oxidation The process of combining with oxygen. The removal of one or more electrons from an ion or an atom.

pediment An eroded bedrock surface that slopes away from the base of mountains in arid regions and is thinly or discontinuously covered by alluvium.

pediment gravel The gravel derived from the mountains uphill that form the cover on a pediment.

pegmatite A very coarse-grained igneous rock, generally containing the same minerals as granite, that commonly occurs in dikes or veins.

periglacial Refers to areas, conditions, processes, and deposits adjacent to the margin of a glacier.

permeable Having pores that permit fluids to pass through.

petrified wood Fossilized wood, formed when wood is buried and replaced by an equal volume of mineral matter.

petroglyph Writings or drawings chipped or scraped into the surface of rock faces. Usually the markings are made in the veneer of dark rock varnish on the face of lighter-colored rock for good contrast.

phenocryst One of the larger, isolated crystals in a porphyritic igneous rock.

piedmont Lying or formed at the base of mountains. A piedmont alluvial plain is formed at the foot of a mountain range by the merging of several alluvial fans.

plagioclase A feldspar mineral group (aluminum silicate with variable amounts of calcium and sodium), whose members comprise some of the most common rock-forming minerals. Plagioclase luster is glassy to pearly, and ranges from colorless to white to gray to yellowish and flesh-red.

plate tectonics The processes or mechanisms by which the Earth's lithosphere (upper crust) is broken up into a series of rigid plates that move over the asthenosphere (lower crust, upper mantle).

playa A dry lakebed floored by fine sediments formed in a desert basin that has internal drainage.

pluton Any body of igneous rock that has formed beneath the surface of the earth by consolidation of magma, regardless of shape or size.

porphyritic An igneous rock that has coarse crystals in a finely crystalline or glassy groundmass.

potash A mineral (potassium carbonate).

potassium feldspar Refers mainly to the minerals orthoclase, sanidine, microcline or adularia, the feldspars rich in potassium.

Precambrian The eon spanning the time from the formation of the earth to the start of the Paleozoic. More than 80 percent of the Earth's estimated 4.5 billion years of age is Precambrian.

psilomelane A mineral, an oxide of manganese. It is a black mineral with an opaque, sub-metallic luster, and rarely exhibits an apparent crystal structure. It readily soils the hands.

pumice A natural glassy froth made by gases escaping through a viscous magma. Its chemical composition is the same as granite or rhyolite.

pyroclastic A general term applied to volcanic materials that have been explosively or aerially ejected from a volcanic vent. Also, a general term for the class of volcanic rocks made up of these materials.

pyrolusite The principal ore of manganese, (manganese dioxide). It has an opaque, metallic luster; is iron-black; and fractures into splinters. Crystal forms include radiating fibers or columns, reniform coatings, dendritic shapes, or granular massive. It readily soils the hands.

pyroxene A group of common silicate minerals (containing varying amounts of magnesium, iron, calcium, aluminum, and sodium) that are light green to black.

quartz monzonite A granular plutonic rock that resembles and is related to granite. Its major constituents are orthoclase, plagioclase and quartz, with minor quantities of biotite, hornblende, apatite, and zircon.

rapakivi A texture originally described in Finnish granites. In typical specimens large flesh-colored potassic feldspars occur as rounded crystals a few centimeters in diameter and are mantled with white sodic plagioclase. These feldspars are embedded in a matrix that has normal granitic texture, but consists chiefly of quartz and colored minerals.

reverse fault An inclined fault along which the hanging-wall block has moved upward relative to the footwall.

rhyolite A fine-grained igneous rock with the same composition as granite.

rhyolitic *See rhyolite*

right-lateral fault A strike-slip fault in which relative motion is such that to an observer looking directly at (perpendicular to) the fault, the motion of the block on the opposite side of the fault is to the right.

rock Any naturally formed, solid aggregate of one or more minerals.

rock varnish A thin, dark, shiny coating consisting mainly of manganese and iron oxides, formed on the surfaces of stones and rock outcrops in various climatic regions (from deserts to cold, periglacial climates) after varying lengths of exposure.

rutile A metallic mineral (titanium oxide). It varies from red to brown to black, has a submetallic luster, and is usually subtranslucent.

sandstone A clastic sedimentary rock made up of sand-sized particles.

sedimentary rock A consolidated accumulation of rock and mineral grains and organic matter that has been transported and deposited by wind, water, or ice, or a rock that has been formed by chemical or organic precipitation.

sericite A fine-grained variety of mica, usually muscovite, occurring in small scales and flakes, commonly formed by alteration of feldspars.

shale A very fine-grained, laminated, clastic sedimentary rock made up of clay-sized particles, none of which are larger than 4 microns. Shale tends to break along parallel planes.

sheared Said of deformation wherein different parts of the same object have been forced to split and slide past each other along a plane.

shield volcano A volcano with a low, flat, broad shape, formed by the build-up of many thin lava flows.

silt A clastic (made of individual particles) sediment in which most of the particles are between 1/16 and 1/256 mm in diameter.

siltstone A very fine-grained, consolidated, clastic sedimentary rock composed predominantly of silt-size particles.

slickensides Striated or highly polished surfaces on hard rocks abraded by movement along a fault.

soft sediment deformation Deformation (of bedding layers, for instance) that occurs in sediment before it hardens into sedimentary rock.

specular hematite A variety of the mineral iron oxide, hematite, that occurs in tabular or disklike crystals having a gray, foil-like, metallic luster.

sphene A calcium titanium silicate mineral, generally yellow to orange, that is found in small amounts in igneous rocks.

spherulite A small spherical aggregation of one or more minerals that is formed by the radial growth of crystals in a rigid glass about a common center or inclusion. Such structures are especially common in the glassy groundmass of silicic lava flows and in obsidian.

stock A body of intrusive igneous (plutonic) rock that is similar to, but smaller than, a batholith.

strata Layers or tabular beds of sedimentary rock that consist of approximately the same kind of material throughout, and that are distinct from the layers above and below.

stratification The layered arrangement of sediments, sedimentary rocks, or extrusive igneous rocks.

stratovolcano Also called composite volcano. Volcanos that emit both fragmental material and viscous lava, and that build up steep conical cones.

striated Solid rock that has had parallel grooves cut into it during movement of fault planes or of glacial ice.

strike The direction, measured as an angle from true north, of a horizontal line in the plane of an inclined rock unit, joint, fault or other structural plane. It is perpendicular to the dip.

strike-slip fault A high-angle fault along which displacement has been horizontal. See right-lateral and left-lateral strike-slip fault.

subduction zone A convergent plate boundary at which a slab of oceanic lithosphere is being pushed beneath another plate (continental or oceanic) and carried down into the mantle of the Earth.

syncline A downfold with a troughlike form. The youngest rock will be found in the center of the fold, with progressively older rocks exposed away from the center.

talus Coarsely broken rock debris from rockfalls or slides that forms an apron sloping outward from the cliff that supplies it.

tear fault A strike-slip fault that trends transverse to the strike of the deformed rocks.

thrust fault A low-angle reverse fault with the fault plane dipping less than 45 degrees.

topographic slope The slope of the local land surface or relief.

trilobite A marine arthropod that lived during the Paleozoic Era; characterized by its three-part (tri-lobed) body.

tuff A rock formed of compacted volcanic fragments. A general term for all consolidated pyroclastic rocks.

unconformably Having the relation of unconformity to the underlying rocks. The overlying rocks did not succeed the underlying strata in immediate order of age and in parallel position.

unconformity A substantial gap or break in the geologic record. A surface within a sedimentary sequence that records a period of nondeposition or erosion.

upper plate The hanging wall or upper side of an inclined fault.

vent The conduit and orifice through which volcanic materials (lava, gas, water vapor) reach the Earth's surface.

volcanic ash *See ash, volcanic*

volcanic dome *See dome*

volcanic neck The solidified material filling a vent or pipe of an inactive volcano. This hard igneous rock may resist erosion better than the mountain mass originally encompassing it and eventually stand alone as a column, tower, or crag.

volcanic plug Necks consisting of a monolithic mass of solidified volcanic rock.

wad An impure mixture of manganese and other oxides. It contains 10-20% water, is generally soft and black, and readily soils the hands.

wash Another term for a shallow streambed with steep sides cut into unconsolidated sediments. This kind of streambed usually carries water only after brief, local precipitation.

zircon A silicate mineral, zirconium silicate, that generally occurs in rocks as tiny grains in trace amounts.

Bibliography

Adams, G.F., and Wyckoff, J., 1971, Landforms: New York, Golden Press, 160 p.

Allen, G.L., and others, 1945, Utilization of Three Kids manganese ore in the production of electrolytic manganese: U.S. Bureau of Mines Report of Investigations 3815, 579 p.

American Geological Institute, 1974, Dictionary of Geological Terms: Garden City, N.Y., Anchor Press/Doubleday, 545 p.

Anderson, R.E., 1973, Large-magnitude late Tertiary strike-slip faulting north of Lake Mead, Nevada: U.S. Geological Survey Professional Paper 794, 18 p.

Anderson, R.E., 1977, Geologic map of the Boulder City 15-minute quadrangle, Clark County, Nevada: U.S. Geological Survey Map GQ-1395.

Armentrout, J.M., Cole, M.R., and Terbest, H., Jr., eds., 1979, Cenozoic paleogeography of the western United States—Pacific coast paleogeography symposium 3: Society of Economic Paleontologists and Mineralogists, Pacific Section, 335 p.

Armstrong, R.L., 1970, Geochronology of Tertiary igneous rocks, eastern Basin and Range province, western Utah, eastern Nevada and vicinity, U.S.A.: Geochimica et Cosmochimica Acta, v. 34, p. 203-232.

Atkin, B.C., and Johnson, J.A., 1988, The Earth—Problems and Perspectives: Palo Alto, Calif., Blackwell Scientific Publications, 452 p.

Axen, G.J., 1984, Thrusts in the eastern Spring Mountains, Nevada—Geometry and mechanical implications: Geological Society of America Bulletin, v. 95, p. 1202-1207.

Axen, G.J., 1986, Thrust faults and synorogenic conglomerates in the southern Spring Mountains, *in* Field trip guide to the geology of southern Nevada: National Association of Geology Teachers, Far West Section meeting, Oct. 3-5, 1986, Las Vegas, Nev., p. 16-22.

Axen, G.J., 1987, The Keystone thrust and Red Spring thrust faults in the La Madre Mountain area, eastern Spring Mountains, Nevada: Geological Society of America Centennial Field Guide, v. 1, Cordilleran Section, p. 57-60.

Axen, G.J., 1989, Reinterpretations of the relations between the Keystone, Red Springs, Contact, and Cottonwood faults; eastern Spring Mountains, Clark County, Nevada—discussion: The Mountain Geologist, v. 26, no. 3, p. 69-70.

Bell, J.W., 1978, Geologic constraints map of the Las Vegas SE Quadrangle: Nevada Bureau of Mines and Geology Map 3Am.

Bell, J.W., 1981, Subsidence in Las Vegas Valley: Nevada Bureau of Mines and Geology Bulletin 95, 84 p.

Bell, J.W., and Smith, E.I., 1980, Geological map of the Henderson Quadrangle, Clark County, Nevada: Nevada Bureau of Mines and Geology Map 67.

Bezy, J.V., 1978, A guide to the desert geology of Lake Mead N.R.A.: Southwest Parks and Monuments Association, Globe, Ariz., 67 p.

Bingler, E.C., 1977, Geologic map of the Las Vegas SE Quadrangle: Nevada Bureau of Mines and Geology Map 3Ag.

Bingler, E.C., and Bonham, H.E., 1973, Reconnaissance geologic map of the McCullough Range and adjacent areas, Clark County, Nevada: Nevada Bureau of Mines and Geology Map 45.

Bissell, H.J., 1969, Permian and Lower Triassic transition from shelf to basin (Grand Canyon, Arizona to Spring Mountains, Nevada), *in* Baars, D.L., ed., Geology and natural history of the Grand Canyon region: Four Corners Geological Society Guidebook, Fifth Field Conference, p. 135-169.

Bohannon, R.G., 1984, Nonmarine sedimentary rocks of Tertiary age in the Lake Mead region, southeastern Nevada and northwestern Arizona: U.S. Geological Survey Professional Paper 1259, 72 p.

Bohannon, R.G., and Bachhuber, F., 1979, Road log from Las Vegas to Keystone thrust area and Valley of Fire via Frenchman Mountain, *in* Newman, G.W., and Goode, H.D., eds., Basin and Range Symposium and Great Basin Field Conference: Rocky Mountain Association of Geologists and Utah Geological Survey, 1979, p. 579-596.

Brenner, E.F., and Glanzman, R.K., 1979, Tertiary sediments in the Lake Mead area, Nevada, *in* Newman G.W., and Goode, H.D., eds., Basin and Range Symposium and Great Basin Field Conference: Rocky Mountain Association of Geologists and Utah Geological Survey, 1979, p. 313-323.

Burchfiel, B.C., and Davis, G.A., 1988, Mesozoic thrust faults and Cenozoic low-angle normal faults, eastern Spring Mountains, Nevada and Clark Mountains thrust complex, California, *in* Weide, D.L., and Faber, M.L., eds., This extended land—geological journeys in the southern Basin and Range: Field Trip Guidebook, Geological Society of Nevada, Cordilleran Section Meeting, Las Vegas, Nev., 1988, p. 87-106.

Burchfiel, B.C., Fleck, R.J., Secor, D.T., Vincelette, R.R., and Davis, G.A., 1974, Geology of the Spring Mountains, Nevada:Geological Society of America Bulletin, v. 85, p. 1013-1022.

Burchfiel, B.C., and Royden, L.H., 1984, The Keystone thrust fault at Wilson Cliffs, Nevada is not the Keystone thrust—implications: Geological Society of America Abstracts with Programs, v. 16, no. 6, p. 458.

Campagna, D.J., and Aydin, A., 1991, Tertiary uplift and shortening in the Basin and Range; the Echo Hills, southeastern Nevada: Geology, v. 19, p. 485-488.

Carlson, H.S., 1974, Nevada Place Names—A Geographical Dictionary: Reno, Nev., University of Nevada Press, 282 p.

Carr, M.D., and others, 1986, Early Middle Jurassic limit for movement on the Keystone thrust, southern Nevada: Geological Society of America Abstracts with Programs, v. 18, no. 5, p. 345.

Cleveland, G.B, 1975, The flash flood at Nelsons Landing, Clark County, Nevada: California Geology, v. 28, p. 51-56.

Cline, G.G., 1963, Exploring the Great Basin: Reno, Nev., University of Nevada Press, 254 p.

Davis, G.A., 1973, Relations between the Keystone and Red Spring thrust faults, eastern Spring Mountains, Nevada: Geological Society of America Bulletin, v. 84, p. 3709-3716.

Dohrenwend, J., 1989, Rates and patterns of piedmont evolution in the southwest Basin and Range, *in* Late Cenozoic evolution of the southern Great Basin: Nevada Bureau of Mines and Geology Open-File Report 89-1, p. 151-152.

Domenico, P.A., Stephenson, D.A., and Maxey, G.B., 1964, Groundwater in Las Vegas Valley: University of Nevada, Desert Research Institute Technical Report No. 7, 53 p.

Drobeck, P. A., and others, 1988, Gold deposits of the Las Vegas region, *in* Weide, D.L., and Faber, M.L., eds., This extended land—geological journeys in the southern Basin and Range: Field Trip Guidebook, Geological Society of America, Cordilleran Section Meeting, Las Vegas, Nev., 1988, p. 65-86.

Duebendorfer, E.M., and Black, R.A., 1992, The kinematic role of transverse structures in continental extension: An example from the Las Vegas Valley shear zone, Nevada: Geology, v. 20, p. 1107-1110.

Duebendorfer, E.M., Sewall, A.J., and Smith, E.I., 1990, The Saddle Island detachment: An evolving shear zone in the Lake Mead area, Nevada, *in* Wernicke, B.P., ed., Basin and Range extension near the latitude of Las Vegas, Nevada: Geological Society of America Memoir 176, p. 77-97.

Duebendorfer, E.M., and Simpson, D.A., 1994, Kinematics and timing of Tertiary extension in the western Lake Mead region, Nevada: Geological Society of America Bulletin (in press)

Duebendorfer, E.M., Smith, E.I., and Faulds, J.E., 1993, Introduction to the area north of I-40: between Lake Mead, Nevada and Needles, California, *in* Sherrod, D.R., and Nielson, J.E., eds., Tertiary stratigraphy of highly extended terranes, California, Arizona, and Nevada: U.S. Geological Survey Bulletin 2053 (in press).

Duebendorfer, E.M., and Wallin, E.T., 1991, Basin development and syntectonic sedimentation associated with kinematically coupled strike-slip and detachment faulting, southern Nevada: Geology, v. 19, p. 87-90.

Earl, P.I., 1986, This was Nevada: Reno, Nev., Nevada Historical Society, 192 p.

Evans, D.B., 1971, Auto tourguide to the Lake Mead National Recreation Area: Southwest Parks and Monuments Association, Globe, Ariz., 39 p.

Feuerbach, D.L., and Smith, E.I., 1987, Late-Miocene Fortification Hill basalt, Lake Mead area, Nevada and Arizona—source areas and conduit geometry: Geological Society of America Abstracts with Programs, v. 19, no. 6, p. 376-377.

Fiero, G.W., 1976, Nevada's Valley of Fire: Las Vegas, Nev., KC Publications, 32 p.

Fiero, B., 1986, Geology of the Great Basin: Reno, Nev., University of Nevada Press, 198 p.

Gilluly, J., Waters, A.C., and Woodford, A.O. , 1959, Principles of Geology: San Francisco, W.H. Freeman and Co., 435 p.
Glancy, P.A., and Whitney, J.W., 1986, Las Vegas Wash—dynamic evolution of a southern Nevada drainage channel: Geological Society of America Abstracts with Programs, v. 18, no. 6, p. 615.
Glass, M., and Glass, A. , 1981, Touring Nevada: Reno, Nev., University of Nevada Press, 253 p.
Hamblin, W.K., 1975, The Earth's Dynamic Systems—A textbook in physical geology: Minneapolis, Minn., Burgess Publishing Co., 578 p.
Hansen, M.W., 1979, Crinoid shoals and associated environments, Mississippian of southern Nevada, *in* Newman, G.W., and Goode, H.D., eds., Basin and Range Symposium and Great Basin field conference: Rocky Mountain Association of Geologists and Utah Geological Survey, 1979, p. 259-266.
Harrill, J.R., 1976, Pumping and ground-water storage depletion in Las Vegas Valley, Nevada, 1955-74: Nevada Department of Conservation and Natural Resources, Water Resources Bulletin 44, 70 p.
Harrill, J.R., and Katzer, T., 1980, Groundwater map of the Las Vegas SE Quadrangle: Nevada Bureau of Mines and Geology Map 3Af.
Harrington, M.R., 1933, Gypsum Cave, Nevada: Southwest Museum Papers No. 8, 197 p.
Harrington, M.R., 1937, Ancient tribes of the Boulder Dam Country: Southwest Museum Leaflets, No. 9, 13 p.
Haynes, C.V., 1967, Quaternary geology of the Tule Springs area, Clark County, Nevada, *in* Wormington, H.M., and Ellis, D., eds., Pleistocene studies in southern Nevada: Nevada State Museum, Anthropological Papers, No. 13, p. 15-104.
Hewett, D.F., and Webber, B.N., 1931, Bedded deposits of manganese oxides near Las Vegas, Nevada: Nevada Bureau of Mines and Geology Bulletin 13, 17 p.
Hogan, J., and Bachhuber, F.W., 1981, Vegetation map of the Las Vegas SE Quadrangle: Nevada Bureau of Mines and Geology Map 3Ae.
Hunt, C.B., McKelvey, V.E., and Weise, J.H. , 1942, The Three Kids manganese district, Clark County, Nevada: U.S. GeologicalSurvey Bulletin 936-L, 319 p.
Jaeger, E.C., 1957, The North American Deserts: Stanford, Calif., Stanford University Press, 308 p.
Katzer, T., 1981, Flood and related debris flow hazards map of the Las Vegas SE Quadrangle: Nevada Bureau of Mines and Geology Map 3Al.
Katzer, T., Harrill, J.R., Berggren, G., and Plume, R.W., 1985, Groundwater map, Las Vegas SW Quadrangle: Nevada Bureau of Mines and Geology Map 3Bf.
Langenheim, R.L., Jr., 1963, Mississippian stratigraphy in southwestern Utah, and adjacent parts of Nevada and Arizona, *in* Guidebook to the geology of southwestern Utah: Intermountain Association of Petroleum Geologists 12th Annual Field Conference, p. 30-42.
Lanner, R.M., 1987, Trees of the Great Basin: Reno, Nev., University of Nevada Press, 215 p.
Levy, M., and Christie-Blick, N., 1989, Pre-Mesozoic palinspastic reconstruction of the eastern Great Basin (western United States): Science, v. 245, p. 1454-1462.
Little, E.L., Jr., 1968, Southwestern Trees—A guide to the native species of New Mexico and Arizona: U.S. Department of Agriculture, Forest Service, Agriculture Handbook No. 9, 109 p.
Longwell, C.R., 1928, Geology of the Muddy Mountains, Nevada: U. S. Geologic Survey Bulletin 798, 151 p.
Longwell, C.R., 1949, Structure of the northern Muddy Mountains area, Nevada: Geological Society America Bulletin v. 60, p. 923-968.
Longwell, C.R., 1974, Measure and date of movement on Las Vegas Valley shear zone, Clark County, Nevada: Geological Society of America Bulletin, v. 85, p. 985-990.
Longwell, C.R., Pampeyan, E.H., Bowyer, B., and Robert, R.J. , 1979, Geology and mineral deposits of Clark County, Nevada: Nevada Bureau of Mines and Geology Bulletin 62, 218 p.
MacMahon, J.A., 1988, The Audubon Nature Guides—Deserts: New York, Alfred A. Knopf, 638 p.

Marzolf, J.E., 1983, Changing wind and hydrologic regimes during deposition of the Navajo and Aztec Sandstones, Jurassic(?), southwestern United States, *in* Brookfield, M.E., and Ahlbrandt, T.S., eds., Eolian sediments and processes: Developments in sedimentology, v. 38, Elsevier, Amsterdam, p. 635-660.
Marzolf, J.E., 1988, Reconstruction of Late Triassic and Early and Middle Jurassic sedimentary basins—southwestern Colorado Plateau to eastern Mojave Desert, *in* Weide, D.L., and Faber, M.L., eds., This extended land - geological journeys in the southern Basin and Range: Field Trip Guidebook, Geological Society of America, Cordilleran Section Meeting, Las Vegas, 1988, p. 177-200.
Matti, J.C., and Bachhuber, F.W., 1985, Geologic map of the Las Vegas SW Quadrangle: Nevada Bureau of Mines and Geology Map 3Bg.
Matti, J.C., Bachhuber, F.W., Morton, D.M., and Bell, J.W., 1987, Geologic map of the Las Vegas NW Quadrangle: Nevada Bureauof Mines and Geology Map 3Dg.
Mawby, J.E., 1967, Fossil vertebrates of the Tule Springs site, Nevada, *in* Wormington , H.M., and Ellis, D., eds., Pleistocene studies in southern Nevada: Nevada State Museum, Anthropological Papers, No. 13, p. 105-128.
Maxey, G.B., and Jameson, C.H., 1948, Geology and water resources of the Las Vegas, Pahrump, and Indian Springs Valley, Clark and Nye Counties, Nevada: Nevada Department of Conservation and Natural Resources, Water Resources Bulletin 5, 128 p.
McKelvey, V.E., Weise, J.H., and Johnson, V.H. , 1949, Preliminary report on the bedded manganese of the Lake Mead region, Nevada and Arizona: U.S. Geological Survey Bulletin 948-D, p. 83-101.
McLane, A.R., 1974, A bibliography of Nevada caves: Center for Water Resources Research, Desert Research Institute, University of Nevada System, Reno, Nev., 99 p.
Mehringer, P.J., Jr., 1965, Late Pleistocene vegetation in the Mojave Desert of southern Nevada: Journal Arizona Academy Science, v. 3, no. 3, p. 172-188.
Mifflin, M.D., 1988, Region 5, Great Basin, *in* Back, W., Rosenshein, J.S., and Seaber, P.R., eds., Hydrogeology, v. O-2, The Geology of North America: Geological Society of America, Boulder, Colo., p. 69-78.
Mifflin, M.D., and Wheat, D.D., 1979, Pluvial lakes and estimated pluvial climate of Nevada: Nevada Bureau of Mines and Geology Bulletin 94, 57 p.
Mills, J.G., 1985, The geology and geochemistry of volcanic and plutonic rocks in the Hoover Dam 7 1/2 minute quadrangle, Clark County, Nevada and Mojave County, Arizona [M.S. thesis]: University of Nevada, Las Vegas, 119 p.
Mindling, A.L., 1965, An investigation of the relationship of the physical properties of fine-grained sediments to land subsidence in Las Vegas Valley, Nevada [M.S. thesis]: University of Nevada, Reno, 90 p.
Mindling, A.L., 1971, A summary of data relating to land subsidence in Las Vegas Valley: University of Nevada Desert Research Institute Publication, 55 p.
Moehring, E.P., 1989, Resort City in the Sunbelt—Las Vegas, 1930-1970: Reno, Nev., University of Nevada Press, 313 p.
Montgomery, C.W., 1990, Physical Geology: Dubuque, Iowa, W.C. Brown Publishers, 555 p.
Moore, D. , 1976, Lost City: Nevada Magazine, p. 26-62.
Mozingo, H.N., 1987, Shrubs of the Great Basin: Reno, Nev., University of Nevada Press, 342 p.
Nevada Department of Minerals and Nevada Bureau of Mines and Geology, 1993, Major mines of Nevada 1992: Nevada Bureau of Mines and Geology Special Publication P-4., 27 p.
Paher, S.W., 1970, Nevada ghost towns and mining camps: Berkeley, Calif., Howell-North Books, 484 p.
Papke, K.G., 1987, Gypsum deposits in Nevada: Nevada Bureau of Mines and Geology Bulletin 103, p. 14-16.
Papke, K.G., and Bell, J.W., 1978, Energy and mineral resources map of the Las Vegas SE Quadrangle: Nevada Bureau of Mines and Geology Map 3Ah.
Patterson, A., 1992, A field guide to rock art symbols of the greater Southwest: Boulder, Colo., Johnson Printing Co., 256 p.

Quade, J., 1986, Late Quaternary environmental changes in the upper Las Vegas Valley, Nevada: Quaternary Research, v. 26, p. 340-357.
Reisner, M., 1986, Cadillac Desert—The American West and its Disappearing Water: New York, Viking Press, 582 p.
Rentz, L.H., and Smith, F.J., 1980, Plants of the Virgin Mountains: U.S. Bureau of Land Management, 51 p.
Reynolds, M.W., and Dolly, E.D., eds., 1983, Mesozoic paleogeography of the west-central United States—Rocky Mountain Paleogeography Symposium 2: Society of Economic Paleontologists and Mineralogists, Rocky Mountain Section, 573 p.
Rowland, S.M., 1986, Paleozoic, Mesozoic, and Cenozoic stratigraphy of Frenchman Mountain, Clark County, Nevada, *in* Field trip guide to the geology of southern Nevada: National Association of Geology Teachers, Far Western Section Meeting, Oct. 3-5, 1986, Las Vegas, Nev., p. 1-14.
Rowland, S.M., 1987, Paleozoic stratigraphy of Frenchman Mountain, Clark County, Nevada: Geological Society of America Centennial Field Guide—Cordilleran Section, 1987, p. 53-56.
Rowland, S.M., 1988, Southern Nevada's evolving natural landscape: Nevada Public Affairs Review, no. 1, p. 33-39.
Secor, D.T., 1962, Geology of the central Spring Mountains, Nevada [Ph.D. thesis]: Stanford University, Stanford, Calif.
Shutler, R., Jr., 1967, Archeology of Tule Springs, *in* Wormington, H.M., and Ellis, D., eds., Pleistocene studies in southern Nevada: Nevada State Museum, Anthropological Papers, No. 13, p, 297-303.
Skinner, B.J., and Porter, S.C., 1989, The Dynamic Earth—An introduction to physical geology: New York, John Wiley & Sons, 540 p.
Smith, E.I., 1982, Geology and geochemistry of the volcanic rocks in the River Mountains, Clark County, Nevada and comparisons with volcanic rocks in nearby areas, *in* Frost, E.G., and Martin, D.C., eds., Mesozoic-Cenozoic tectonic evolution of the Colorado River region, California, Arizona, and Nevada: Cordilleran Publishers, p. 41-54.
Smith, E.I., 1984, Geologic map of the Boulder Beach Quadrangle, Nevada: Nevada Bureau of Mines and Geology Map 81.
Smith, E.I., 1986, Geology of the River, Eldorado and McCullough Ranges, Clark County, Nevada, *in* Field trip guide to the geology of southern Nevada: National Association of Geology Teachers, Far West Section meeting, Oct. 3-5, 1986, Las Vegas, Nev., p. 23-35.
Smith, E.I., 1986, Road log and field guide from Henderson to Hoover Dam via Lake Mead, *in* Field trip guide to the geology of southern Nevada: National Association of Geology Teachers, Far West Section meeting, Oct. 3-5, Las Vegas, Nev., p. 36-64.
Smith, E.I., Schmidt, C.S., and Mills, J.G., 1988, Mid-Tertiary volcanoes in the Lake Mead area of southern Nevada and northwestern Arizona, *in,* Weide D.L., and Faber, M.L., eds., This extended land—geological journeys in southern Basin and Range: Field Trip Guidebook, Geological Society of America, Cordilleran Section Meeting, Las Vegas, 1988, p. 107-122.
Smith, E.I., Feuerbach, D.L., Naumann, T.R., and Mills, J.G., 1990, Mid-Miocene volcanic and plutonic rocks in the Lake Mead area of Nevada and Arizona; production of intermediate igneous rocks in an extensional environment, *in* Anderson, J.L., ed., The nature and origin of Cordilleran magmatism: Geological Society of America Memoir 174, chapter 10, p. 169-194.
Sowers, J.M. , and others, 1988, Geomorphology and pedology on the Kyle Canyon alluvial fan, southern Nevada, *in* Weide, D.L., and Faber, M.L., eds., This extended land—geological journeys in the southern Basin and Range: Field Trip Guidebook, Geological Society of America, Cordilleran Section Meeting, Las Vegas, 1988, p. 137-157.
Spaulding, W.G., 1985, Vegetation and climates of the last 45,000 years in the vicinity of the Nevada Test Site, south-central Nevada: U.S. Geological Survey Professional Paper 1329, 83 p..
Stevens, J.E., 1988, Hoover Dam—An American Adventure: Norman, Okla., University of Oklahoma Press, 326 p.

Stewart, J.H., 1980, Geology of Nevada: Nevada Bureau of Mines and Geology Special Publication 4, 136 p.
Taylor, E.M., 1989, Late Quaternary paleoclimate studies—geologic problems and questions, *in* Late Cenozoic evolution of the southern Great Basin: Nevada Bureau of Mines and Geology Open-File Report 89-1, p. 153.
U.S. Soil Conservation Service, 1982, Soils map of the Las Vegas SE Quadrangle: Nevada Bureau of Mines and Geology Map 3Ad.
Van Devender, T.R., 1977, Holocene woodlands in the southwestern deserts: Science, v. 198, p. 189-192.
Van Devender, T.R., and Spaulding, W.G., 1979, Development of vegetation and climate in the southwestern United States: Science, v. 204, p. 701-710.
Walker, T.R., and Honea, R.M., 1969, Iron content of modern deposits in the Sonoran Desert—A contribution to the origin of Red Beds: Geological Society of America Bulletin, v. 80, p. 535-544.
Wallin, E.T., Duebendorfer, E.M., and Smith, E.I., 1993, Tertiary stratigraphy of the Lake Mead region, *in* Sherrod, D.R., and Nielson, J.E., eds., Tertiary stratigraphy of highly extended terranes, California, Arizona, and Nevada: U.S. Geological Survey Bulletin 2053 (in press).
Wernicke, B., Axen, G.J., and Snow, J.K., 1988, Basin and Range extensional tectonics at the latitude of Las Vegas, Nevada: Geological Society of America Bulletin, v. 100, p. 1738-1757.
Wernicke, B., Guth, P.L., and Axen, G.J., 1984, Tertiary extensional tectonics in the Sevier thrust belt of southern Nevada *in* Lintz, J., Jr., ed., Western geological excursions, volume 4: Geological Society of America 1984 annual meeting, Reno, Guidebook, volume 4, p. 473-510.
Wheeler, S.S., 1982, The Nevada Desert: Caldwell, Idaho, The Caxton Printers, Ltd., 168 p.
Wright, F., 1981, Clark County—The changing face of southern Nevada: Las Vegas, Nev., Nevada Historical Society, 38 p.
Wright, F., 1984, The Pioneering Adventure in Nevada: Las Vegas, Nev., Nevada Historical Society, 29 p.
Zdon, A., and Kepper, J., 1991, Las Vegas to Hoover Dam, and the Frenchman Mountain area, *in* Geology of the Las Vegas region: American Association of Professional Geologists, Nevada Section, 1991 Field Trip, p. 1-10.